STEPPING STONES

Stories for Assembly
by
LINDA ALLEN
with suggestions for
follow-up activities by
JOHN FERGUSON

Batsford Academic and Educational Ltd
London

Typeset by Photobooks (Bristol) Ltd.
and printed in Great Britain by
Biddles Ltd
Guildford, Surrey

for the publishers
Batsford Academic and Educational Ltd,
an imprint of B.T. Batsford Ltd,
4 Fitzhardinge Street
London W1H 0AH

ISBN 0 7134 1265 8

STEPPING STONES

Contents

Introduction

I was first introduced to Linda Allen's delightful short stories when I was asked to comment on some material being considered for publication. I was completely captivated by her work, as were the children in my school.

The intention was for the book to be a selection of stories with moral implications, that could be used either in school assemblies or just as stories to be read and discussed by children from 5 to 9 years of age. As a teacher with nearly twenty years' experience of working with children of first school age range, I have often been faced with the prospect of presenting a school assembly without a single original thought in my head. I felt that the concept of a book like the one Linda envisaged was a wonderful innovation; it was a book I could see many of my colleagues reaching for. I made this observation, and suggested that the stories could also be used to stimulate follow-up work across the curriculum, which was also Linda's philosophy for the book's application.

On the basis of these comments, I was invited to work on the book with Linda, and it has been a most enjoyable exercise. I have involved the children at school in every stage of the book's production. I have used them in a market research exercise, by reading each story to the school. The children have been instrumental in selecting the stories that have been included.

The aims for the book are three-fold. The stories have strength enough to warrant being published on their own and the book can be used just as a source of short stories with moral themes. The majority of the stories can also be adapted for use as plays for school assembly. In my own school we have used many in just this way. We have also dramatized "Father Christmas and the Ice Goblins" for part of our Christmas Concert. The stories are versatile, in so far as the number of characters can be made flexible, and scenery is not altogether necessary. Hence the scale of production can range from a sketch to a classic performance.

Thirdly, for each story there is an outline of some of the follow-up possibilities that are presented. These are only suggestions and I am sure that the experienced teacher will be able to enlarge upon them and suggest alternatives. There are times, however, when even the most energetic value some assistance. I hope that some of the activities will prove helpful.

The moral themes that are woven into the stories include Honesty, Loyalty, Consideration for Others, Caring and Sharing, Cheerfulness in Adversity, Helpfulness, Concern for the Environment, Tolerance, Politeness, Kindness, the Importance of Friendships, Resisting Temptation, Patience, Gentleness, Unselfishness and Dependability. These are issues which are generally accepted as being of vital importance. At the beginning of each story the moral implications it contains are printed in parentheses.

The stories have been grouped in chapters so that they can be used in connection with a topic or project that is being developed. In this way, the stories can be used either to stimulate follow-up work or in connection with work that is already in progress.

The chapter titles are fairly open-ended. They are very general headings which I am sure feature regularly in the cycle of popular first school topics. Chapter One is entitled "Real Life", because the stories are about people in what could almost be real-life situations. The stories in this chapter can be used in connection with a range of research topics, including Essential and Emergency Services, People Who Work For Us, Conservation and Pollution.

Chapter Two is "Weather and the Seasons", which covers subjects that must feature regularly in the timetable of most schools. Other topics in conjunction with which these stories can be used could be Rainbows, Colour, Light Reflections and Growing Things.

Chapter Three is about "Animals" – real, mystical and toy. These stories can accompany or stimulate a variety of ecological and wild life studies.

Chapter Four contains stories about different aspects of "Fantasy" – witches, fairies, pixies and magicians. These stories might stimulate topics on Ourselves, Growing Up and Diet.

In the second part of the book, I have attempted to show how some of the stories can be used in connection with extended project or topic work. I have placed a lot of emphasis on scientific follow-up, because this is an area of the curriculum for which we have come in for some criticism from the H.M.I. in *Primary Education in England* and *Education 5 to 9: an illustrative survey of 80 first schools in England*, both published by H.M.S.O. in 1978 and 1982 respectively. I am sure this criticism is justified and that the fault is due mainly to lack of confidence on the part of teachers to embark on scientific topics. It was my intention in this section to provide teachers with simple step-by-step scientific programmes, which they can follow with confidence.

I have included some examples of the work that has resulted in my school from Linda's stories. There are a few pieces of creative writing from each chapter and a set of photographs of our production of "Father Christmas and the Ice Goblins" to indicate how, with a little effort and the minimum scenery, even in a small rural school like mine it is possible to stage quite lavish presentations using the stories.

The final part of the book contains cross-referencing with publications, materials and apparatus that can be used with groups of stories; and a list of songs and pieces of music that are suitable for use in assembly or as musical follow-up.

Acknowledgment

Linda Allen and John Ferguson would like to thank:

Joy Brooks, for the original idea for the book and for her advice, suggestions and assistance with each of the stories

John Hollingworth, for the hard work he put into drawing up the suggestions of pieces of music to accompany the topic work.

PART ONE

CHAPTER ONE

Real Life

The Cake That Made People Jump

(*Cheerfulness in Adversity*)

One day Mrs Jenkins made a cake. She used a bit of this and a bit of that, and a pinch or two of something else, and she mixed them all together and put them in the oven.

When she took the cake out of the oven, it smelt delicious. She couldn't resist cutting just a small slice for herself, but she had not eaten much of it before she started to jump.

First she jumped over the dog, who was lying asleep on the rug. "I'm sorry, Tag," she said. "I hope I didn't frighten you. I can't think what came over me."

Tag opened one eye and wagged his tail, which was his way of saying, "I don't mind at all."

Mrs Jenkins jumped over the baby, who was playing on the floor. "My poor child!" cried Mrs Jenkins. "Do forgive me!"

The baby only gurgled and laughed. He thought it was very funny to see his mother jumping over things. Mrs Jenkins went on jumping for a few more minutes. Then she sat down to think about it. "It must be the cake," she decided. "I have never done any jumping before, but I quite enjoyed that." And then she went shopping and forgot all about it.

When Mr Jenkins came home, the first thing he saw was the cake on the table. "That cake looks delicious," he said. "I'd like a nice big piece of that for my tea."

Mrs Jenkins cut a piece of cake and Mr Jenkins ate it. Suddenly, he got up from the table and jumped over the piano. Then he sat down again. "I wonder why I did that?" he said. "I never felt like jumping over the piano before."

"I think it has something to do with the cake," confessed Mrs Jenkins. "I had a piece this morning and I jumped over all sorts of things."

"But what did you put in the cake?" cried Mr Jenkins.

"Oh, just a bit of this and a bit of that and a pinch or two of something else," said Mrs Jenkins. "But the truth of the matter is that I can't remember exactly what I did put in it."

"Never mind," said Mr Jenkins. "It's never happened before and I don't suppose it will happen again."

"I'm so glad you don't get cross when things go wrong," said Mrs Jenkins. "You are always so cheerful, my dear."

"I always like to make the best of things," responded Mr Jenkins. "What's the use of getting cross about things like that?"

The following morning Mrs Jenkins fancied another piece of cake. She took it out of the cupboard and put it on the table. Mr Jenkins looked at it rather doubtfully. "Are you going to eat that cake?" he asked.

"Just a small slice, my dear," said Mrs Jenkins. "Will you have some too?"

"Well, maybe just a little," said Mr Jenkins. "I have to do some gardening today and if I eat too much of that cake I might jump into the garden pond."

"Oh, I'm sure it won't have the same effect now that it's stale," Mrs Jenkins assured him.

But it did.

Mrs Jenkins had scarcely swallowed her first bite when she rushed out of the front door and jumped over the postman, who was just delivering the letters. The postman looked amazed. He had never seen Mrs Jenkins jumping before. He asked her if anything was the matter. "No," she said, cheerfully. "It's the cake I made yesterday that makes me jump."

"Don't you find it rather inconvenient?" asked the postman.

"Not at all," laughed Mrs Jenkins. "I've got nothing else to do today."

At that moment, Mr Jenkins came jumping out of the house. He jumped down the steps and over the flower beds and all along the garden path. Then he came back to the front door. "Good morning," he said to the postman.

"Good morning," responded the postman. "Mrs Jenkins has just been telling me about the cake she baked yesterday. I could do with a cake like that myself. I have so many letters to deliver this morning that it would be a great help if I could jump over a few garden gates."

"In that case," said Mrs Jenkins, "you shall have what's left of my cake. I can always make another one when I feel like jumping again."

So the postman took the remainder of the cake and off he went. He nibbled pieces of the cake all day and he jumped over hedges and fences and garden gates, and he delivered his letters in double-quick time.

Mrs Jenkins often tried to make another cake that made people jump, but she was never successful. She could never again get the ingredients quite right.

She did, however, make a cake that made her sing, and another one that made Mr Jenkins climb trees, and at Christmas she baked one that made everyone dance, but Mr Jenkins never complained. As he said, it was being so cheerful under difficulties that made his world go round.

And Mrs Jenkins agreed.

*   *   *

Follow-up Discussion
The children will probably need some guidance into understanding the moral of this story, but being cheerful in adversity is something that they should be made aware of at an early age. Putting it into practice is equally very difficult for children. It is a quality that comes only with maturity and experience and then even only in certain people.

The point of the story can be further illustrated by referring to those people who cheerfully contend with serious illness or injury. There are many examples throughout the country, like Lancashire's Pat Seed. On having cancer diagnosed, she devoted all her time and energy to raising money to provide a scanner to help in the early diagnosis of the disease in fellow sufferers.

Language Development and Creative Writing
Mrs Jenkins made other cakes which made people sing, climb trees and dance. The children could discuss what magical ingredient they would like to bake into a cake.

Environmental Studies and Science
Mrs Jenkins used a most unscientific method of baking and yet when we cook we are directly involved with many scientific processes, such as weighing, measuring, mixing and following instructions.

Just cracking an egg can provide sufficient stimuli for a lesson. With supervision, the children could do some baking.

The children could also do some research into jumping animals.

Mathematics
The story provides an opportunity for mathematics in connection with current British, Commonwealth, European, Olympic and World jumping records. The children can measure these records in the playground, compare them, see how many jumps of their own jumps would be needed to equal the records.

Music
Part of Vaughan Williams' *The Wasps* is called "The March of the Kitchen Utensils" and it is very suitable for use with young children.

Drama and Movement
The antics which Mr and Mrs Jenkins and the postman get up to after eating the cake make this a difficult story for adaptation for use as a play.

There are aspects of the story that can be used in a movement and mime lesson, such as "jumping".

Isabella's Oak

(Concern for the Environment)

Many, many years ago a little girl was out walking with her father in woods near their home. As they paused to rest, her father pointed with his walking stick to a large tree. "Just imagine," he said, "how long this oak tree has been growing here, Isabella. Perhaps for two hundred years, perhaps longer." He stooped and picked up an acorn which had fallen from the tree. "And isn't it wonderful," he went on, "to think that this magnificent tree started life as one of these?"

Isabella took the acorn from her father's hand. Her eyes were wide with wonder. "From one of these?" she repeated, and then asked curiously, "If I planted one of these – this one – would it grow into an oak tree?"

"Yes," replied her father, "there is every possibility that it would."

Isabella kept the acorn in her hand. They walked back towards home. When they came to the lane leading back to their house she said, "Please, Father, may I plant my acorn here, just on the corner of the lane?"

Her father made no objection, and he made a hole in the earth with his stick, into which Isabella dropped the acorn; then she covered up the hole with earth. That night she wrote about the incident in her diary.

Winter came and covered the ground with snow and ice. Isabella forgot about the acorn, but one day in summer when they passed by the spot again she suddenly remembered it. "I wonder if my acorn is growing?" she cried, running to the spot where she had planted it. To her delight she saw a slender stem growing out of the grass, topped by two oak leaves. There was no doubt that it was her very own oak tree. She was delighted. When she got home she told all her relations and friends about it, so that in time, as the tree grew taller and more sturdy, it became known as Isabella's Oak.

Time went by. Isabella grew up and had children of her own. The tree was now very tall and strong, and everyone in the village had come to call it Isabella's Oak. Most of the younger children, however, were unaware that the tree was named after the old lady who lived in the Manor House, who had planted an acorn when she was a little girl, and when Isabella died there were few people left who remembered the circumstances which had led to the planting of the tree. Sometimes a newcomer to the village would ask why the tree was so named, and the answer was, "Oh, it was named after some old lady who used to live in the village, but who she was we can't quite remember."

The village grew in size and number. The village school which had stood in the lane for many years became too small to take in all the children who now lived there, and it was decided to extend it. The architect made his plans. "Here," he said, "we shall have a new classroom, and here a corridor, another classroom, and an assembly hall. Of course, the old tree will have to come down, but that's no problem. We shall have a much better school without it."

But the children of the village school were very fond of the old tree. They loved to play in its shade when the sun was hot; they liked to watch its leaves come in the springtime, and fall in the autumn; they liked the creatures that lived in and around its branches – the squirrels, the wood pigeons, the beetles and butterflies. It was unthinkable that it should be chopped down, and all those creatures deprived of their home. They spoke to their teacher about it. "We don't want the tree to come down," they said. "It's our tree. It belongs to the school. Nobody else has a tree in their school garden with a proper name."

Their teacher, Mrs Grace, agreed with them. She had come from the town to teach at the village school, so she knew nothing about Isabella, but when the children began to ask questions about the tree she, too, began to wonder why the tree was so named. "Perhaps we could make it a sort of project?" she suggested. "Shall we try to find out if there really was a person called Isabella, and who she was?"

The children were enthusiastic. "Yes!" they cried.

"Very well," said Mrs Grace. "The first thing to do is to enquire of the older people in the village if they know why the tree has such a name. Perhaps your grandparents would know something about it."

So the children asked the old people, and at last a very old lady was found who said, "When I was a child I asked my grandpa about Isabella's Oak, and he told me that he thought it was named after a lady who lived at the Manor House."

Mrs Grace said, "We must go to the Manor House. It's a museum now, but perhaps we shall find a clue there as to who Isabella was and why the tree was named after her." That afternoon the children went to the Manor House Museum. They found that the museum was displaying costumes of earlier ages, books, pictures, writing materials. One room contained children's costumes and playthings, and in a glass case near the window was a selection of children's work. Among the items in the case was an old diary. "Look, children," said Mrs Grace, "Here is a diary written by a child over a hundred years ago." The children crowded round. The handwriting was beautifully neat and well-formed, and was open at a page in October. There was an account of a party on one side of the page, and then, towards the bottom of the right-hand side the children found these words: I went for a walk with Father today and we planted. . . . But there the page ended.

"Mrs Grace!" cried one of the children. "Suppose it was an oak tree that they planted! Suppose it was Isabella who wrote that diary!"

Mrs Grace agreed that it was possible. She went to ask the curator if he would allow her to take a closer look at the diary, and when he heard why the children were so interested he opened the glass case and took out the diary.

Mrs Grace looked as excited as the children as she turned the page. ". . . an acorn at the corner of the lane," she read. "Father says it will grow into an oak tree one day, and that it may survive for three hundred years."

Mrs Grace looked at the fly leaf of the book and read, "Isabella Bateman, her diary." She looked at the children. "So it *was* named after a real person," she said thoughtfully. "There *was* a real Isabella."

On their way back to school the children were quiet. They were thinking about the little girl who had planted an acorn and watched it grow into an oak tree. When they got back to school they each wrote a story about Isabella, and next day they drew pictures of the tree. Mrs Grace helped them to make a frieze, and when their project was quite finished they invited someone to come and look at it. Their visitor was the architect who was designing the new school buildings. "We thought you ought to know something of the history of the oak tree," said Mrs Grace.

"Please don't chop down Isabella's Oak," pleaded the children.

For a few minutes the architect was silent. He was reading one of the stories about Isabella. When he looked at the children he said, "I'm going to tell you something quite amazing, children. When I came here today I thought I knew what I was going to say to you. I was going to explain that it would be impossible to change my plans and that, reluctant as I might be, the tree would have to go. I always knew that the tree was known as Isabella's Oak, but I never knew why until just now. But that is not all. If Isabella really did live at the old Manor House, then I am a direct descendant of hers. How can I chop down a tree that was planted by my great-great-great-grandmother? For that is who Isabella must have been." He told the children to follow him outside, and there he picked up an acorn from underneath the tree. "I shall take this home with me," he said, "and plant it in my garden in memory of my relation Isabella."

"You ought also to make a note of it in your diary," smiled Mrs Grace.

"I'll do that," promised the architect, "and I'll alter my plan for the new school buildings."

How happy the children were! But Mrs Grace had one more suggestion to make. "If you can find a place where an oak tree could grow without causing an obstruction, why not take an acorn from Isabella's Oak and plant it there? Isabella may not have realized it at the time, but she was planting happiness and pleasure for several generations following her, and I believe it is up to each one of us to try to do the same."

*   *   *

Follow-up Discussion

This story provides teachers with a perfect opportunity to dwell upon the vitally important issue of conservation. It should lead naturally into discussions on every aspect of the subject. The Country Code would also be an integral part of this discussion. The children could consider the damage that can be caused to both people and animals by thoughtless disposal of litter. A study of the list of endangered species will reveal that, in the interests of "nature study", many flowers and animals have become quite rare. The common frog is no longer common, as a glaring example.

Language Development and Creative Writing
Work in language development and creative writing could be along the same lines as the follow-up discussion. Conservation is a very broad as well as a particularly important issue which can never receive too much emphasis.

Environmental Studies and Science
This story provides an ideal opportunity to start an in-depth study into trees. There are many activities that can be pursued in connection with a project of this nature. It is also a subject that is well-documented for both the children and the teachers.

Art and Craft
Permanent records of the shapes of various leaves, tree bark and twigs can be made. An impression is first made in plasticine, and this is surrounded with a small "wall" of plasticine or a "collar" of cardboard. Plaster of Paris is poured into this and when it is set, the plasticine mould is carefully removed, leaving a plaster relief. These can now be painted. The plaques can be made into attractive wall decorations by inserting an opened paper clip into the plaster before it sets.

There are, of course, many other activities that can be done with leaves, bark and twigs which are already common practice in many schools.

Drama, Movement and Music
This story could be dramatized, but will probably have more impact if it is read to the children by a teacher.

For movement lessons, trees blowing in the wind can be developed.

The Boy Who Couldn't Tell The Truth

(Honesty)

There was a boy called Frederick who couldn't tell the truth. Everything he said was a lie.

"My mother has baked some bread this morning," he said to the baker, so the baker didn't deliver any bread.

"We have plenty of milk," he told the milkman, so the milkman didn't leave any milk.

He told the postman that they were going to live in China, so the postman stopped delivering letters.

It was all very difficult for Frederick's mother. She didn't know what to do. She tried to explain to Frederick that it was just as easy to tell the truth as it was to tell a lie, but he didn't seem to understand.

She took him to see the doctor.

"What seems to be the trouble?" asked the doctor.

"It's Frederick," explained Frederick's mother. "He can't tell the truth."

"Dear me!" exclaimed the doctor. "I have heard of people who can't tell the time, but never anyone who couldn't tell the truth. How very interesting." And he told Frederick to stick out his tongue. "Well, that seems to be all right," said the doctor. "Bring him to see me every Thursday and I'll see what I can do."

He gave Frederick some green medicine to take before breakfast every morning and some pink medicine to take after supper every night, but it didn't do any good at all. Frederick still went on telling lies all over the place.

When the time came for Frederick to go to school he told his teacher that his name was Jellybaby and that he lived at the top of the Post Office Tower. Now the teacher was a very clever lady, and instead of saying that he was a wicked boy to tell such untruths she gave him a writing book with the name Jellybaby written on the front.

All the other children began to call him Jellybaby. They laughed at him. They teased him.

"My name isn't Jellybaby," he cried at last. "My name is Frederick."

But nobody believed him. They thought he was still telling lies.

Frederick's mother took him to see the doctor again. "Is he getting any better?" he asked.

"Oh, no, Doctor," said Frederick's mother. "He seems to be worse."

So the doctor gave Frederick some white medicine as well, to be taken with his school dinners on Thursdays.

One day it was Frederick's birthday. But the postman didn't bring any birthday cards because he thought that Frederick had gone to live in China. And the milkman didn't bring any milk because he was never quite sure when Frederick's mother wanted it. The baker never called at Frederick's house, so there was no bread for making sandwiches for a birthday party.

Frederick went to school.

"It's my birthday," he told the teacher.

She didn't believe him.

"It really is my birthday," he said to the other children, "and my mother says you can all come to my birthday party."

But the children just laughed at him. "Jellybabies don't have birthdays," they said.

"Will *you* come to my birthday party?" he asked the teacher.

"Oh, no, I couldn't do that," said the teacher. "I couldn't possibly climb up to the top of the Post Office Tower."

"I don't live at the top of the Post Office Tower," cried Frederick. "I live at number sixty-five, Mill Street, and my name is Frederick and it really is my birthday. Won't you *please* come to my birthday party?"

The teacher shook her head sadly and went on with her work.

When Frederick went home from school his mother said, "Why, where are the children? Didn't you bring them to your birthday party?"

"They wouldn't come," said Frederick. "They didn't believe me."

"Well, we can't have a birthday party without any friends," said Frederick's mother, "so you'd better go and wash your hands and face and go to bed early instead."

Poor Frederick! He washed his hands and face. He sat down on the stairs. He decided that telling lies was a very silly thing to do.

And just at that moment there came a knock at the door. It was the postman. "I've just heard that Frederick hasn't gone to live in China, after all," he said. "Here are some birthday cards for him."

The baker came up the garden path. "I've brought some bread," he said. "I heard that it was Frederick's birthday today."

The milkman came too. "One crate of strawberry milk shakes," he said, "especially for Frederick's birthday party."

And who should come in at the kitchen door but Frederick's teacher and all his friends from school, all crowding round and wishing him many happy returns of the day! They brought a birthday cake with candles on it and his name written on the top in blue icing.

Frederick was cured at last. His mother said it was all on account of the cleverness of his teacher and the children in his class, but the doctor didn't agree. He said it was the white medicine taken with school dinners on Thursdays, and as far as I know he is still giving it to people who don't know how to tell the truth.

*   *   *

Follow-up Discussion
This story illustrates the stupidity of telling lies. What did telling lies achieve for Frederick, other than loneliness and unhappiness? When he did tell the truth, people did not believe him, just as with Matilda and the fire and the boy who cried "Wolf".

The children should be able to relate to this story and will be able to discuss whether Frederick was happier when he was telling lies or when he was telling the truth.

Language Development and Creative Writing
Frederick's lies do show some degree of imagination. His choice of name and address are most amusing. The children could explore this in a lesson. They could choose a name and address for themselves, to see who can find the funniest.

Environmental Studies and Science
This story can be used in connection with a project on "People Who Work For Us". It introduces some of the people who either provide a service or are traders in vital supplies.

Art and Craft
The children could paint pictures of bottles of different-coloured medicines.

Drama and Movement
This story can very easily be dramatized for use in assembly.

The Children of Mulberry School

(Consideration for Others)

The children who went to Mulberry School were very disorderly. There wasn't a well-behaved child among them – not one. The teachers didn't know what to do with them, and the poor Headmaster was so reluctant to go to school every morning that he used to stamp and say to his wife, "I don't want to go to school this morning. I won't go to school." Then his wife had to be patient with him. She would take him by the hand all the way to school and when they got to the gate she would kiss him and say, "Now be very good in school today and you shall have your favourite pudding for supper tonight."

But the Headmaster would lock himself in his room at the school and listen to the children shouting and throwing things about, and would not come out for anything. The teachers didn't know where to find the books or pencils, or who was counting the dinner money, or what to do if one of the children was sick on the floor, or anything. It was terrible.

The children never learnt anything, of course. They were far too busy making a noise and being a thorough nuisance to everybody. And then one day the School Inspector came.

The first thing he noticed was that the children were so ill-mannered, and the second thing he noticed was that he couldn't get into the Headmaster's room.

He knocked on the door.

"Go away!" cried the Headmaster from within.

The School Inspector was shocked. "You can't tell *me* to go away," he shouted back.

"Why not?" cried the Headmaster.

"Because I am the School Inspector," was the reply.

The Headmaster's door opened the merest crack and the Headmaster peeped out. "Are you really the School Inspector?" he said. "You're not one of those dreadful children pretending to be a School Inspector, are you?"

"Certainly not!" exclaimed the School Inspector. "However, I quite understand what you mean, so open the door and let me come in."

The Headmaster opened the door and the School Inspector went inside, and they plotted together. When the School Inspector came out, he patted the teachers on the head and told them not to worry because things would soon be better, and he went away.

Next morning the Headmaster's wife was very surprised to find that her husband went to school quite willingly. He had a big smile on his face. When he got to school he called all the children and the teachers into the hall and told them what he and the School Inspector had decided to do. "Today," he went on, "the teachers will take the place of the children, and the children will take the place of the teachers. What do you say to that?"

"Hooray!" cried the children.

"Hooray!" cried the teachers.

Then the children rushed on to the platform where the teachers were standing and pushed them all off. "Can anybody play the piano?" said the children among themselves, but nobody could, because they had all been too lazy to try. So they couldn't sing a morning hymn.

"Well, never mind," said one of the children, "We'll read something to them instead." But nobody could do that, either, because they had all been too disobedient to learn to read. One girl said that she could recite a poem, but when she tried the teachers were making so much noise that she couldn't be heard, and she burst into tears and went and sat in a corner by herself.

Next, the children tried to decide who should be the Headmaster, but *everybody* wanted to be the Headmaster because they thought it was such an easy job, and whilst they were arguing about it the teachers were running wild all over the school. Mr Punchington was pretending to be a wild animal and chasing Mrs Bandycoot all over the place, saying that he was going to bite off her head. Mrs Jollifer and Miss Gumbell were rolling about on the floor, pulling one another's hair. And the Headmaster was sitting on top of the piano pretending to be a monkey.

"Be quiet!" the children cried. "We have to call the registers and find out who is staying to dinner."

The teachers would not be quiet. They didn't even stop to listen to what the children were saying, but went on behaving as badly as before. One boy, who was trying very hard indeed to be a good teacher, asked if anybody had brought a note to school that morning, and the teachers said that they had *all* brought notes but that they had lost them on the way to school.

When the dinner-ladies came they were all so frightened at what was going on that they turned and ran off home as fast as their legs would carry them; so nobody got any dinner.

At the end of the day the children were exhausted, and very, very hungry. They had shouted so much to try to control the noisy teachers, that they had lost their voices, and they sat down, every one of them, on the floor in the hall, and sucked their thumbs.

When the teachers saw that the children had learnt their lesson they came in quietly and the Headmaster spoke to the children. "Do you think that the School Inspector's idea was a good one?" he asked.

The children could not speak, but some of them nodded and some of them shook their heads.

"Shall we try the same thing tomorrow?" enquired the Headmaster.

This time *all* the children shook their heads.

And from that day onwards the children of Mulberry School were as good as it is possible for children to be – that is, most of the time.

*   *   *

Follow-up Discussion
Children think they have the monopoly of being mischievous. This story provides the opportunity for frank discussion between teachers and children.

Being honest with the children about some of our own childhood misdemeanours could help the younger generation to realize that the adults with whom they associate played many of the pranks that are played by the schoolchildren of today. Emphasis must, of course, be placed on harmless childhood pranks.

Language Development and Creative Writing
This story can lead into lively discussion and creative writing about what the children would expect to find in their perfect school.

Discussion could also centre around what both the teachers and the children regard as the role of the school.

Environmental Studies

A research project could be done into how school life has changed and what traditions remain.

Research into "playground culture" could prove interesting. How have the games, rhymes and traditions been handed down through generations of schoolchildren without any reference to adults?

Letters to schools in other parts of the country could result in a regional map showing variations in elimination rhymes.

Another avenue worthy of exploration could be discussion of crime and punishment. What do the children think of the methods of punishment used in school? Can the children suggest more suitable methods?

The story of George Washington can be told to the children in connection with this story.

Drama

"The Children of Mulberry School" should make an amusing and enjoyable play for use in assembly.

The Chief of All the Chiefs

(Cheerfulness in Adversity, Kindness to Animals)

One day, in a country where all the people lived in tribes, the chiefs had gathered together in a circle to welcome a new chief. When he arrived, the company were astonished to find that he was only a boy. The eldest chief spoke to him, fixing him with a proud and terrible eye. "My name," he said, "is Koleidon, which in the language of my tribe means The Powerful Warrior; I am the son of Kol, The Slayer of Beasts."

"And I," said the next in line, "am Day-froll-gith, which means Biter of Dragons." And so it was with all the chiefs; each one telling his awful name, with pride in his fighting achievements.

"Now," said Koleidon, "tell us your name and what it means in the language of your fathers."

The lad looked straight back at Koleidon and for a moment his eyes twinkled. In his tribe there were no such fine-sounding names and they had never seen any reason to go about fighting wild beasts and making life uncomfortable for themselves. Life in his tribe was peaceful and gentle. "My name," he said, "is Yonkiponk, and in my language it means The Bringer of Merriment, son of Yonki, Who Laughed at all Men." And he sat down on the ground in the circle, keeping his face quite straight.

"Yonkiponk?" the chiefs murmured. "The Bringer of Merriment? What kind of name is that for a great new chief?" They looked with disfavour upon one whose name was so lacking in manliness.

"How do you come by such a name?" demanded Koleidon.

Yonkiponk (as he had called himself) was not at all abashed by the question. "In my tribe," he said, "as soon as the children are of an age to experiment with the sounds of their tongues, they choose their own names. You must honour my name."

The chiefs didn't know what to do. They were not at all sure whether or not the boy was laughing at them, but as he continued to sit there without further speech, Koleidon thought he had better attempt to get rid of the boy somehow. He felt that there was no place among the great chiefs for one so weak-spirited as the boy appeared to be. "In order to be accepted as a chief among us," he told the lad, "you must undergo three trials. First, you must travel alone and unarmed through The Pass of the Roaring Lion, proving yourself more cunning than he. Next, you must swim across the Man-fish Bay, where a certain creature, cleverer than Man, will attempt to entice you away to the open sea. Last of all, you will venture at night into the Plains where the Wild Beasts cry. If you can do all these things, you will be accepted as a member of our brotherhood."

"Those are stern tests," said Yonkiponk cheerfully, "but I have no doubt that I can endure them and return safely."

The chiefs accompanied him to The Pass of the Roaring Lion, watching as he walked into the domain of the king of beasts, and they settled themselves at the entrance to the pass to wait for the snarling of the lion that would tell them that Yonkiponk was no more.

The boy soon met the lion, who sprang down from his rock and bared his teeth in a dreadful warning. "Why, if it isn't a lion!" said Yonkiponk, sitting down on the rock and taking out his dinner. "Perhaps you would like some of this?"

"You should look upon me in fear and trembling," said the lion. "I am Leo, king of the beasts."

"And I am Yonkiponk," retorted the boy, "the Bringer of Merriment. Aren't you hungry?" And he casually got on with his dinner.

The lion rolled over on his back and roared with laughter at the name. The chiefs, waiting in the distance, heard the noise, and were sure that all was over with the boy. They went back to their conference, thinking that they had seen the last of Yonkiponk; but a short time later they were astonished to see him come back and take his place within the circle. "Tomorrow," he said, "I will swim across the Man-fish Bay."

When the sun arose next day, Yonkiponk plunged into the water, and the chiefs stood on a hilltop to watch his progress. He had barely started when a dolphin came up to him and began to swim wildly around him. Yonkiponk welcomed him with delight and asked his name.

"My name," said the dolphin, "is Delphos, and it is my duty to lure you out into the great ocean, where you will die of exhaustion and fear."

"Don't do that," said Yonkiponk. "I am only Yonkiponk. I am not your enemy. Have fun with me."

The dolphin rolled and gambolled about with the boy. He began to laugh, and from that day to this there has been a grin on the face of every dolphin that ever heard the name of Yonkiponk. Delphos was only too happy to guide the merry lad across the waters of the bay, and in no time at all Yonkiponk was making his way back to where the chiefs were waiting for him.

"You have done well," conceded Koleidon, somewhat grudgingly, "but remember that there is yet one test to undergo."

"Tonight," agreed Yonkiponk. "Tonight when the moon rises I will go to the Plains where the Wild Beasts cry."

When night-time came, he set off, and the chiefs made sure that he was well within the range of the hyenas that roared in the plains. Then they retreated with their spears and arrows to a safe watching place. The hyenas came close to the boy, sniffing the air for the scent of his weapons, but when they knew that he had none they approached him even closer and felt his goodwill towards them. "Who are you?" they cried. "Why do you come unarmed into the midst of us? Don't you know that we are wild beasts and that we could tear you to pieces with our sharp teeth?"

"Nonsense," said the boy. "You don't want to eat me. I am only Yonkiponk, and I bring nothing but merriment."

The hyenas screamed with laughter; they laughed until the plains echoed with the sound, and the chiefs felt their blood run cold, for the hyenas had never made sounds like those before. "We shall never see him again," they said. "For all his courage in laughing when he goes into the territory of the wild things, he cannot come out of that alive. He is gone for sure."

But when morning came, the boy came back, and sat down in the centre of the circle, and looked at the chiefs with his twinkling eyes. "Now," he said, "I have proved my courage to your liking, and for that you shall make me the chief of all the chiefs."

The chiefs declared their willingness, for the boy's bravery was far beyond doubt, and asked what he would have them do.

"Nothing," he replied, "except change your names. A bringer of merriment cannot be the chief of such bloodthirsty-sounding chiefs as you. Decide what your new names will be, and come and whisper them into my ear, and before long we shall have the whole world smiling." So the chiefs thought long and hard, and realized that laughing together was much better than fighting; one by one, they came to Yonkiponk and whispered their new names in his ear, and very soon, as he had predicted, the whole world began to smile.

*   *   *

Follow-up Discussion

The idea that bravery can be achieved by good humour and tolerance is a concept that children will have difficulty in comprehending. Trials of strength and fighting are not the only means of establishing superiority.

Judging by the reports of violence from all over the world which fill our newspapers and television newsreels, this is also a concept that needs to be stressed.

The bravery shown by Yonkiponk in successfully passing the three tests set him by the other chiefs could help some of the older children to understand this rather complex issue.

Language Development and Creative Writing

This story was conceived when the author overheard children on the bus experimenting with sounds.

This is a natural part of a child's language development and one that the child thoroughly enjoys. The story provides an opportunity for children to experiment with unusual and original sounds. The children can make up the new non-violent names for all the chiefs.

Nonsense poems by Edward Lear, Lewis Carroll, Spike Milligan and Dr Seuss would be a natural progression. The story could be a stepping stone to the introduction of the old-fashioned parlour game "Charades".

Environmental Studies and Science

The children could do some research into the habitats and lifestyles of the animals mentioned in the story, which can lead into a much wider animal study.

Music

Many nonsense poems have been put to music, which can be learnt in connection with the story.

The use of the syllables in names can be used to establish rhythm patterns.

Art

The story read in conjunction with some of the nonsense poems could provide some very rich stimuli for art and craft.

Drama and Movement
"The Chief of All the Chiefs" is easily adapted for use as a play in assembly. The animals in the three tests will provide the opportunity to use imaginative portrayal.

The children can make up tribal dances for a dance and drama lesson.

Jeremy Jumbletop

(Tolerance, Cheerfulness in Adversity)

Jeremy Jumbletop was a very strange man. He did everything the wrong way round.

He walked backwards. He sat backwards on his chair.

When he went to bed he put on all his clothes, including his hat and his boots, and when he got up he put on his pyjamas and went to work.

He slept in the daytime and worked at night.

All his life people had tried to make Jeremy Jumbletop do things the proper way. "You're very silly, Jeremy Jumbletop," they used to say. "Whoever heard of anyone starting his dinner with pudding and finishing with soup? It's nonsense, and you ought to change your ways."

But Jeremy Jumbletop didn't care. He liked to do things the wrong way round. He was very happy. Even when he read the newspaper upside down it made perfect sense to him, and although he stood on his head to watch television he enjoyed it just as much as anyone else.

The strange thing was that some of his ways were very useful to other people. Because he was so good at skating backwards he was able to teach people to skate forwards. And he was quite a champion at tug-of-war, because pulling backwards came so naturally to him.

He went on holiday in the winter-time, of course, riding with his back to the engine in the train, and arriving at the seaside in the middle of the night. He stayed in a caravan which he had turned upside down because he liked it better that way, although he had to admit that he did keep falling out of his bunk when he had just nodded off to sleep.

One night when he was on holiday at the seaside he decided to go for a walk. He was walking backwards along the beach when he thought he heard a cry for help. He was a little surprised at first, because it was two o'clock in the morning, very, very dark, and bitterly cold, and all the people who did things the proper way round were all tucked up in bed.

He listened again. Yes, there was certainly somebody calling.

"Who's there?" he shouted above the noise of the wind and the rain.

"Help me!" said a voice.

"Where are you?" asked Jeremy Jumbletop.

"Here I am," answered the voice. "Up here, on the cliff. I'm stuck on a ledge and it's so dark that I dare not move an inch for fear of falling down."

"I'll come and get you," said Jeremy Jumbletop.

"No, no!" cried the voice. "You couldn't possibly find me. Go along to the coastguard's house and get him to bring some lights and a good strong rope. That's the only way I can be saved."

"Oh, very well," said Jeremy Jumbletop. "I'll do as you say, but I'm afraid the coastguard will be very cross when I wake him up."

He ran backwards along the beach until he came to the coastguard's house. As he had feared, the coastguard was not at all pleased to be woken up in the middle of such a dreadful night.

"How did you come to be on the beach at this time of night?" he said.

"I was taking a walk," said Jeremy Jumbletop.

"What a silly thing to do," said the coastguard. "I never heard of such a thing. Are you quite sure there is a man trapped on a ledge?"

"Oh yes," said Jeremy Jumbletop.

The coastguard roused several of his friends and they set off all together along the top of the cliff until they came to the place where the man was trapped. "He's down there," said Jeremy Jumbletop.

Sure enough, they heard the trapped man crying out. Lights were brought to the scene and the men peered over the edge of the cliff. "Can you wait until daylight?" they cried.

"No, no, I shall freeze to death," came the reply. "Do hurry."

The men shook their heads. "We can't go down there," they said. "Even with ropes we shall have to lead him backwards along the ledge and who is going to do that? We need someone who has eyes in the back of his head!"

And they all looked at Jeremy Jumbletop.

"You can walk backwards," they said. "And you can climb downwards without looking where you are going."

"Of course I can," said Jeremy Jumbletop. "I told the man I would help him before, but he didn't know who I was and he didn't trust me."

When the man on the ledge heard that Jeremy Jumbletop was coming down to help him he was delighted. "I have heard of you, Jeremy Jumbletop," he said.

Jeremy Jumbletop tied a rope around his waist and went backwards down the cliff quite easily. He took hold of the man's hands and led him along the ledge to safety.

Everybody said how brave Jeremy Jumbletop had been, but he only shook his head. "It was quite easy," he said.

All the same, the people in the seaside town made a great fuss of him. They gave him a dinner at seven o'clock in the morning, and he had upside-down cake and sausages with the skins inside. Then he put on his very best suit and went to bed.

Jeremy Jumbletop was no doubt a very strange man. He went on doing things the wrong way round for the rest of his life, but nobody made fun of him any more, because he had proved how very useful he could be.

The queen gave him a medal, and can you guess where he wore it?

That's right. On his back.

* * *

Follow-up Discussion
Jeremy Jumbletop was a very strange fellow, but was he wrong in doing things his way? From the story, it is apparent that he was able to use his extraordinary talents to other people's advantage.

In the world we live in there are an increasing number of people who adopt unconventional ways of dressing and behaving. Are they necessarily wrong? It is only when it hurts or inconveniences other people that we can say it is harmful. Even the most conventional person can upset others by a careless remark. The demands of society as we know it are such that we have to learn to tolerate other people's beliefs, opinions and ways of life.

This story can be used to promote discussion about tolerance.

Language Development and Creative Writing
Jeremy's ability to watch television or read his newspaper upside down can lead into looking at and discussing words. An explanation of the meaning of "palindromic" can result in a search for words that qualify.

Can the children find words that can be turned around to make another meaningful word? Some words when reversed make lovely nonsense starters. This exercise could be developed into work on anagrams and even codes and ciphers.

Environmental Studies and Science
The codes and ciphers study can be extended to include mathematics.

One thing that Jeremy did that is not strange is work at night. The coastguard, if he was doing his job properly, should not have been asleep. There are lots of people who work on night shift and this could form the basis of a research topic.

Art and Craft
Upside down or mirror drawing and paintings could be a development from this story. These could prove to be an interesting and valuable exercise in observational and manipulative skills.

Drama and Movement
This story involving a cliff rescue could be rather difficult to use as an assembly sketch, but it provides the teacher with a wealth of material for use in a movement and drama lesson.

Monty Mean and Generous Jack

(Consideration for Others)

Once upon a time there was a man called Monty Mean. His real name was Montague Flynn, but everybody called him Monty Mean because he never gave anything away. He wouldn't help the poor. He wouldn't share anything with anybody.

He was a very rich man, and he was always buying things for himself. Some of the things he bought were no good to him, but would he give them away? Of course not. He just used to store them up in his house and gloat over them.

As the years went by he began to get rather short of space in his house. All the cupboards were full of things he never used. The bath was full of jam. The hall cupboard was full of walking sticks. He couldn't get into the pantry for all the tins and bottles he had in there. And he couldn't get into bed because it was piled high with boots and shoes.

Next door to Monty Mean lived a man called Generous Jack. It was easy to see why he was called that, because his house was almost empty. He had given everything away except a few cooking pots, a bed and a chair. He had very little money, but what he had he shared with those who had none, and he never bought anything for himself except what he needed to keep himself alive.

The time came when Monty Mean's house was so full that he couldn't get into any of the rooms. The staircase was stacked from top to bottom with possessions. The hall was packed to the ceiling. There was just enough space behind the front door for him to lie down in, and there he used to sleep.

He went out one afternoon to buy a few more things. It was quite dark when he got back home. He pushed his way into his house, arranged his new possessions around him, and went to sleep.

In the morning he awoke and looked round. "How I should like a nice cup of tea," he said to himself, but he couldn't get into his kitchen. "How I should like to watch my television set," he said, but he couldn't get into the living room. "How I should like a nice hot bath," he went on, but how could he have a bath in a bath full of jam?

"Never mind," he consoled himself, "I'll go out and buy myself something instead."

He tried to get to his feet, but he found that all his boxes and packages were pressing round him. He tried to open the front door, but the things he had bought the day before were holding it tightly shut. He couldn't get up and he couldn't get out.

Oh dear, what could he do? He began to cry out, "Help, help!" and fortunately, Generous Jack heard his cries and came running round to see what was the matter.

"I'm stuck in here!" cried Monty Mean. "I can't open my own front door. I can't move an inch. I shall have to stay here for ever!" And he began to moan and groan.

Generous Jack thought it was time that Monty Mean was taught a lesson. "I'll help you," he said.

"I knew you would," sighed Monty Mean.

"I'll make a bargain with you," said Generous Jack.

"Anything, anything," cried Monty Mean.

"Will you change houses with me?" asked Generous Jack. "You shall have my empty house and I will have your full house. There's a nice warm bed in my house, and a kettle and a teapot in the kitchen, all you need to make yourself comfortable."

"But what about all my beautiful things?" cried Monty Mean. "What about my boots and shoes, my walking sticks, my bath full of jam, and all the other things I have?"

"Don't worry about them," laughed Generous Jack. "I'll give them all away."

"No, no, no!" cried Monty Mean. "I can't do it, I can't!"

"Then you'll just have to stay there," said Generous Jack through the letter box. "I'll come back next week and see how you are getting on."

"No, don't go!" shouted Monty Mean as Generous Jack pretended to go away. "I'll agree to what you say. After all, I can always fill up your house with new things. I shall enjoy doing that."

So Generous Jack got a chopper and chopped down the front door and Monty Mean scrambled out. He ran round to Generous Jack's house to make a nice cup of tea, leaving Generous Jack in possession of his old house.

Time went by. Generous Jack was very happy finding things in the house to give to people who needed them. Monty Mean didn't change his ways, but went on buying things he didn't need, just to look at. He filled up Generous Jack's old house right to the front door again, and Generous Jack emptied Monty Mean's old house, except for a few cooking pots, a bed and a chair.

And can you guess what they did when that happened?

That's right. They changed houses again.

* * *

Follow-up Discussion

This story spotlights the saying that it is "better to give than to receive". This is a concept that children have difficulty in coming to terms with. Very young children are reluctant to share their toys.

Material possessions are not necessarily the recipe for happiness. Jack had just enough to make him comfortable. Monty, on the other hand, had everything and still wanted more and he was not satisfied. Jack derives pleasure from his generosity and from sharing his good fortunes with others.

Generosity is not restricted to sharing material possessions. The children can discuss ways in which they can show consideration for others. Some suggestions would include lending a helping hand, politeness, cheerfulness and giving up free time to sit with an elderly person.

Language Development and Creative Writing

The names "Monty Mean" and "Generous Jack" suggest a game of making up some names – rhyming names, names starting with the same letter or sound.

Environmental Studies and Science

The children could do a project on collections. Some of the older children may already have started their own collections – stamps, coins or postcards. Nowadays, people make collections of such a wide range of different objects and most collectors are so keen on their hobbies that it might be possible to arrange for the children to visit a collector and to see his collection. Local museums often house collections and a visit should be profitable.

The animal kingdom has some collectors amongst its members – the magpie, the jackdaw and the squirrel are but three. A study of animal collectors would be a progression for the "Collections" project.

Art and Craft
The house of Monty Mean, being full of all his possessions, provides some imaginative stimuli for painting. The bath full of jam, the hall cupboard full of walking-sticks, and pantry full of tins and bottles suggest some amusing cartoon paintings.

Drama and Movement
This story has rather limited potential for use as a play, because of the number of characters and the technical problems of the scenery or sets. It should be used as an assembly reading, because the message it carries is an important one.

The Lord Mayor's Clock

(Consideration for Others, Kindness)

One morning in spring Claude the cuckoo-clock maker jumped out of bed and said to his wife, "Hooray, it's my birthday!"

"Yes, dear," replied Lydia, "I know it is, and I have bought you a present."

"A present!" exclaimed Claude. "What is it?"

"Look out of the window," smiled Lydia, "and you'll see."

Claude ran to the window and looked out. "A donkey!" he cried. "Just what I've always wanted."

As he dressed he danced around the bedroom, singing happily to himself, "*I've* got a donkey, *I've* got a donkey!"

Lydia was very pleased that her present had made Claude so happy. "What would you like for breakfast?" she asked. "Something special, perhaps, because it is your birthday?"

"A donkey!" said Claude.

Lydia laughed. "You can't have a donkey for breakfast," she said. "I'll make you some pancakes instead."

Claude went downstairs and threw his arms around his donkey's neck. "You're my very own donkey," he said, "and as it is my birthday today I shall not do any work. I shall take Lydia for a picnic and you shall come with us."

The donkey was very pleased with the idea. There was a look in his eye which told Claude that his donkey was looking forward very much indeed to the special treat. He thought it very likely that his donkey had never been on a picnic before. Claude was just about to run indoors to tell Lydia his plan when he saw the Lord Mayor coming up the garden path.

"Good morning, Mr Lord Mayor," he said. "It's my birthday today, and my wife Lydia has bought me this beautiful donkey as a birthday present. What do you think of him?"

"I haven't time to discuss donkeys," snapped the Lord Mayor, who was a proud and haughty man. "I've come to tell you that I want a new clock, and I want it before seven o'clock this evening."

"But I've already promised my donkey," said Claude, "that I would take him for a picnic, because it is my birthday. Won't tomorrow do?"

"Indeed it will not," frowned the Lord Mayor. "I'm giving a banquet tonight, and I've broken my best clock. What will my guests say if there is no clock in the place?"

"But I only make cuckoo-clocks," Claude reminded him.

"I'm aware of that," said the Lord Mayor. "That is why I have come to you. I thought a cuckoo-clock might amuse my guests. You'd better get started right away. I shall expect you to deliver it before seven."

He strode away down the garden path without another word. Even though he was a Lord Mayor he had very bad manners. The donkey watched him go with a strange look in its eyes, but Claude didn't notice that.

"I'm sorry, old chap," he said. "We shall just have to go for our picnic another day." He sighed. "But it won't be the same as going on my birthday."

After breakfast Claude went into his workshop and started work on the Lord Mayor's clock.

"I declare that donkey is quite devoted to you already, Claude!" exclaimed Lydia at dinner time. "He's been watching you through the open door all morning."

"I'm glad you noticed," whispered Claude. "I was beginning to think it was just my imagination, but he certainly hasn't taken his eyes off me since I began work on the clock. As for me, my mind is so full of donkeys that I'm afraid I shall make a very poor job of the Lord Mayor's clock."

But as Claude worked on, he began to see that the clock was the finest he had ever made. The carving was just right, and the ticking was as quiet as anyone could wish, and the little door where the cuckoo was to pop out opened as gently and easily as a lilac bud in May. When it was quite finished Claude said to the donkey, "I should be very much obliged if you would carry me into town to deliver the clock. I feel very tired after working so hard all day, and it's after six o'clock already."

The donkey seemed willing, so Claude climbed on to his back, and off they went. As they came near to the Lord Mayor's banqueting hall there was a very strange look in the donkey's eyes, but of course Claude, from his position on the donkey's back, couldn't see that.

"I hope you have done the job properly," said the Lord Mayor, when Claude handed over the clock. "Donkeys indeed!" And he went indoors to hang up the clock without offering either Claude or his donkey any refreshment.

"Almost seven o'clock," said Claude to the donkey. "I'll tell you what we'll do. We'll peep through the window of the banqueting house and see what the guests think of my clock when the cuckoo pops out. I didn't have time to test it properly before we set out."

Claude and the donkey went round to the window of the banqueting hall just in time to see the guests waiting for the cuckoo to pop out. The little door opened and out popped the cuckoo. Claude was delighted that his clock was working so well. It was exactly on the stroke of seven.

And then the cuckoo began to call.

And do you know what it said?

"Hee-haw! Hee-haw! Hee-haw!"

The Lord Mayor looked as black as thunder. The guests began to roar with laughter. "Hee-haw, hee-haw, hee-haw, hee-haw!" And then it stopped.

"What have you done to deserve that, Mr Lord Mayor?" enquired the guests, still laughing at him.

"Nothing," he snapped, "absolutely nothing."

Claude rubbed his whiskers thoughtfully. "I wonder," he said, and looked down at the donkey. "I've been making cuckoo clocks these forty years and more, and nothing like this has ever happened before. Did you have anything to do with it?"

The donkey made no response, but as they came away Claude heard the guests making fun of the Lord Mayor. And do you know what *they* were saying?

Cuckoo, cuckoo, cuckoo!

*   *   *

Follow-up Discussion
The Lord Mayor totally disregards the feelings of the clockmaker. He is only interested in himself and his own feelings. With the help of the donkey, the Lord Mayor is made to look foolish in front of his guests.

Many young children find it very difficult to come to terms with sharing when they first come to school. This aspect of consideration of others' feelings is probably the easiest way to approach the follow-up to this story.

Language Development and Creative Writing
Birthdays and presents can be developed as a language and creative writing theme. Extension of the time project into seasons, migration and hibernation can also provide an opportunity for language development and creative writing.

Environmental Studies and Science
The amount of work that can be done on clocks and time is sufficiently vast for it to be developed into a project spanning a whole term and possibly longer. It is also a topic for which there is ample published material.

Mathematics
There is also a vast amount of practical mathematics which can be done in connection with the time theme. Work on telling the time can be extended into digital clocks, twenty-four-hour clocks and calendars.

Art and Craft
The ornate designs on old grandfather clocks could be used to stimulate paintings of clock faces. Night and day and the seasons can give rise to landscape paintings depicting the changes.

Music
Clocks and time figure in many different branches of music, ranging from children's songs to popular and the classics. "My Grandfather's Clock" and *The Clock Symphony* are two well-known examples.

Drama and Movement
This story can be adapted for use as a play in assembly.

The concept of clocks and time also presents the teacher with the opportunity of using clockworks in a movement and mime lesson.

Mr Tootle's Walking Stick

(*Honesty*)

Mr Tootle's walking stick looked like any other walking stick. Only Mr Tootle knew that there was something special about it, but Mr Tootle never mentioned it to anybody. He only smiled and said nothing.

Every morning, the people of the town saw Mr Tootle walking along the High Street and heard his stick going tap-tap-tap, but because it looked such an ordinary stick, nobody bothered to give it a second glance.

One day, Mr Tootle went tap-tap-tapping along the High Street to the Post Office to collect his pension. As he stood at the counter, he propped his stick in a corner so that he could more easily count his money and put it safely away in his pocket. Two boys, who were already late for school, saw the walking stick standing in the corner. "I'm going to take that stick," said Toby.

"But it belongs to that poor old man," protested his friend Joss.

"I don't care," said Toby. "I want it and I'm going to have it," and he darted into the Post Office and picked up the stick. Mr Tootle saw what was happening, but he didn't say a word.

Toby ran outside, laughing in triumph at what he had done, and began to walk along the pavement tap-tap-tapping the stick just as Mr Tootle did when he walked along.

"You're going the wrong way!" cried Joss. "If we don't go to school today you know we shall get into trouble."

"I can't help it!" shouted Toby. "The stick seems to be pulling me away!" He soon disappeared around a corner, and Joss had to go to school on his own. When the teachers asked him where his friend Toby was, he said he didn't know, which was perfectly true, because by that time Toby was miles away, being led into all sorts of uncomfortable places by Mr Tootle's walking stick.

First of all, he was taken to a building site, which was knee-deep in mud. The workmen yelled at him and the guard-dogs barked fiercely. Toby was terrified. He tried to let go of the stick, but somehow he couldn't, and on he went, stumbling sometimes, but never being allowed to stop. Two of the workmen began to chase him, but the stick was dragging him along so swiftly that they soon got left behind and had to give up the chase.

Into the heart of the town went the walking stick, with Toby following unwillingly behind. People laughed to see so young a boy walking along with a stick like an old man, and Toby began to feel foolish, as well as afraid and tired. Before very long, they came to the old church of St Agnes, with its tall bell-tower. The stick took Toby inside the church, through the door at the bottom of the bell-tower, and up the spiral staircase. One, two, three steps he climbed. Four, five, six, and so on until he had climbed one hundred and seven steps, which was the number of saints the man who built the tower could remember by heart. By the time he got to the top Toby was puffing and blowing, but the walking stick refused to let him rest, and straight away led him down again, one hundred and seven saints' steps into the street outside.

"Let me go!" shouted Toby to the stick, and again the people laughed. They thought it was very funny to hear a boy talking to a walking stick.

"Why don't you throw your stick away?" enquired one man.

"You don't seem to like it very much!" laughed another.

"I can't throw it away," replied Toby, "and it isn't my stick."

"Do you mean you stole it?" asked a lady. "Then it serves you right." And all the people stopped laughing and booed him instead.

"Let's follow him," cried one of the crowd, "and see where the stick takes him!"

The walking stick went tap-tap-tapping on, with Toby following, and all the people of the town following *him*. Through the open-air market, and in and out of the buildings, upstairs and downstairs in people's houses, where some of them were having breakfast, and some were in the bath, and right through the fountain in the middle of the square.

At last, to Toby's relief, the walking stick stopped, and when he looked up, he saw that they were back at the Post Office, and there was Mr Tootle sitting on a bench outside, enjoying the sunshine as if nothing at all had happened.

"I'm sorry I took your stick," said Toby, and he really meant it.

Mr Tootle stretched out his hand and took the walking stick from Toby. The people clapped and cheered. "That's taught him a lesson he won't forget," they said, and they were right. Toby never stole anything again. He was once tempted to run off with somebody's bicycle, but then he thought better of it, for who knows where *that* might have taken him!

As for Mr Tootle, he never said a word in explanation. He simply smiled, and tap-tap-tapped his way back home.

*   *   *

Follow-up Discussion
This story illustrates the moral that dishonesty is not the best policy.

Children are always losing things in school and invariably the cry is "Somebody has stolen my. . .". More often than not it has been mislaid, left at home or put down somewhere in school and forgotten. The "stolen" article nearly always turns up.

Those children who have been in this position will have experienced their emotions when they have lost something. As a result, they should be able to describe their feelings in these circumstances. This can be developed into a discussion of what they imagine Mr Tootle's feelings would have been when his walking stick was stolen.

Language Development and Creative Writing
The use of the "tap-tap-tapping" of the walking stick leads naturally into an explanation of onomatopoeia and the discovery of further examples.

Toby's embarrassment gives us an opportunity to introduce discussion about some of the children's embarrassing situations.

Music
The walking stick also suggests work that can be done about musical and rhythmical sounds to be heard around the town.

Drama and Movement
"Mr Tootle's Walking Stick" is a story that will adapt for use as a play in assembly.

There are some aspects of this story which can be used in movement and mime lessons. Walking through knee-deep mud and being dragged along by the walking stick are just two examples.

The Princess Who Looked Down Her Nose

(Consideration for Others, Helpfulness, Politeness)

Long ago there lived a princess who was so proud and haughty that everyone called her The Princess who Looked down her Nose.

She was beautiful and clever, and many suitors came to ask for her hand in marriage, but she looked down her nose at them all and said she would only marry the richest ruler in the world.

Now, The Princess who Looked down her Nose had a younger sister named Lilah, who loved nothing better than to make herself useful. Sometimes she would help the palace baker to bake the bread. At other times she would go into the gardens and help the gardeners with their work. Quite often she was to be seen polishing the silver or dusting the royal staircase. She, too, was beautiful, but not at all proud.

One day a handsome young prince came to the palace to ask the princess to marry him. He saw Lilah gathering apples from the trees in the palace gardens, and thinking her to be the daughter of one of the gardeners, he said to her, "Tell me where I can find The Princess who Looks down her Nose."

"I think you mean my sister, sir!" laughed Lilah, and told him where he might find her.

The Princess who Looked down her Nose listened haughtily to what the young prince said, but sent him away with the usual reply. When the prince went back to his country he told his friend, who happened to be the richest ruler in the world, what had happened. "She is very proud," he said, "but the strange thing is that she has a sister who helps to pick the apples in the palace gardens."

Some time later a king went to the palace. He saw Lilah sweeping the steps, and he thought she must be one of the housemaids, so he asked if she could direct him to The Princess who Looked down her Nose.

Again Lilah laughed. "She is my sister," she said. "Come, I will take you to her."

The Princess who Looked down her Nose told the King that she couldn't think of marrying him because he only had a very small palace and three castles without central heating.

The king went away. He, too, was a friend of the richest ruler in the world, and he went to him to tell his story. "The Princess who Looks down her Nose is beautiful indeed," he said, "but far too proud for me. Yet she has a sister who is quite happy to sweep the palace steps."

A third suitor appeared at the palace, and having entered by the back entrance, found Lilah in the palace kitchen, rolling out the dough for the day's baking. "I have come to see the Princess," he said, supposing her to be one of the kitchen maids.

"I will show you to my sister's apartments, sir," she smiled. "Come this way."

Although this king was the richest so far, The Princess who Looked down her Nose would have nothing to do with him, believing that sooner or later the richest ruler of all would come to the palace to claim her. The king went away thinking very deeply. He was not sorry that he had been rejected by such a proud and haughty girl, but he thought how strange it was that her sister should be so humble. As he happened to be the cousin of the richest ruler in the world, he told him what had happened, including an account of the princess's younger sister who sometimes worked in the palace kitchens.

The richest ruler in the world rode up to the palace. There he saw Lilah dusting the marble staircase.

"I have come to ask for the hand of the Princess in marriage," he said, bowing low.

"You mean my sister, sir," said Lilah rather sadly, for she loved the appearance of this truly majestic king and could hardly bear the thought of his being rejected by her sister.

"Oh no," he replied. "I don't want to marry The Princess who Looks down her Nose. I want to marry you."

Lilah was astonished, but she had fallen instantly in love with the king, and she accepted him at once. He told her that he had liked what he had heard of her from his friends and that he knew she would make a good and gentle queen.

So they were married and lived useful and happy lives, deeply loved by everyone.

As for The Princess who Looked down her Nose – she never married anybody, but went on looking down her nose for the rest of her life.

*   *   *

Follow-up Discussion
The children may need to have the difference between "pride" and "haughtiness" explained. There is, of course, nothing wrong in being proud; in haughtiness there is.

Very few people, if they are honest, can say that they have never been snobbish. Snobbishness is manifest in so many different ways. This could form the basis for a discussion.

Helpfulness is another discussion point that can be developed from this story. Lilah displays the truly virtuous helpfulness. She enjoys baking the bread, working with the gardeners and dusting without expecting any reward. This story could be used to emphasize the point that "Thank you" should be reward enough for helping others.

Language Development and Creative Writing
Children often feel proud and justifiably so. They can be encouraged to talk and write about the things that give them feelings of pride.

Lilah enjoyed helping. Do the children like to help at home? Many children offer to help in school, but in most instances these offers have ulterior motives. "The playground is very cold," "I've fallen out with my friend," "So and so has been teasing me," are just a few of the unspoken reasons. The children could write about having to help at home when there is something much more interesting to do.

Environmental Studies and Science
The story mentions princes, kings and rulers. The children could research heads of state and royal families of the countries of the world.

Art and Craft
A frieze or a collage made up of castles, palaces, stately homes and impressive buildings could follow this story.

Drama and Movement
This is a very good story for adapting as a play for use in assembly.

All the helpful things that Lilah does around the palace could be used in a movement and mime lesson.

The Terrible Traffic Jam

(Consideration for Others)

There was a terrible traffic jam at the village crossroads one day. What a muddle it was! Everybody seemed to be in such a hurry, and everybody seemed to want to go in a different direction.

"Ting-a-ling-a-ling!" tinkled the bicycle. "Please let me come through. I am in a most frightful hurry!"

"Who do you think you are?" demanded the motorbike. "My business is just as important as yours. I have to get somewhere quickly, too, so move aside and let me be on my way."

"Oh no you don't!" hooted the car. "I mean to be first out of this traffic jam and I have no time to waste in talking about it. You'll have to wait your turn, all of you."

"But I can't!" pleaded the bicycle. "My errand, I do assure you, is very urgent, and if only you knew what it was you would move aside and let me come through before you."

"What impertinence!" snapped the car.

"Absolutely," agreed the motorbike.

"Little whippersnapper," put in a van that had cut across all of them. "I don't suppose it has occurred to any of you that I might be delivering urgently-needed goods. I know all about you bicycles and motorbikes and cars, gallivanting off, enjoying yourselves, and thinking you own the road. Well, let me tell you that you don't. We working vehicles have just as much right to be on the roads as you have. Who's causing the hold-up, anyhow?"

"It's the lorry," said the bicycle. "He can't seem to get his front wheels forward, and if he moves backwards he'll bump right into you, I'm afraid."

"Let him try," growled the van. "Just let him try, that's all."

"Are you challenging me?" bellowed the lorry through its exhaust. "Because if you are, I accept." And without another word it backed straight towards the van.

"Stop!" shouted the van.

"Look out!" cried the bicycle.

"Mind what you're doing!" the car hooted.

"Get out of my way," honked the motorbike.

They all pushed and jostled; they backed up and they edged forward, all crying out together that they were in a most desperate hurry; but it seemed that the more they tried the worse their problems became, simply because each one of them thought their journey was the most important.

Whilst they were struggling, another vehicle came up. "Ee-ah-ee-ah-ee-ah!" it moaned. "What's all this? You know who I am. Clear the way there!"

"It's that bossy old fire engine," the motorbike said. "I've had trouble with him before. Thinks he owns the road. Always expects to have a clear way ahead – but I suppose I'd better let him go. That noise is driving me mad."

He backed out of the fire engine's way.

"Thank you," said the fire engine, "ee-ah-ee-ah-ee-ah!"

"Pardon me," said the bicycle to the fire engine. "If I can just cut across you – like this – you may be able to take my place. Mind you, I'm not saying that I think you are more important than I am simply because you make more noise. I want you to understand that."

"Perfectly," said the fire engine. "Eh-ah!"

"I suppose," sighed the car, "there will be no peace for any of us until he's got his way, so here you are, fire engine, come round here. I do it under protest, mind."

"That goes without saying," the fire engine retorted. "Ee-ah-ee-ah!"

The van shivered with irritation. "I am quite sure," it said to the fire engine, "that if you understood *my* mission you would admit that I have the right of way, but as everybody seems to think that you have priority I'll have to let you through."

"No time to debate the point," the fire engine said. "Fire waits for nobody. Ee-ah-ee-ah-ee-ah-ee-ah . . ."

That left only the lorry. It was making a tremendous noise, pretending that it hadn't even heard the fire engine, when suddenly there came another shriek. "Be-bo-be-bo-be-bo-be-bo!"

"Ambulance!" cried all the vehicles together. "Out of the way, lorry, and let the ambulance through."

The lorry gave a huge shudder, swung its front wheels around, and pulled in to the side of the road. The ambulance rushed through the gap, and the fire engine followed it.

"You see?" said the bicycle. "If we had worked it out sensibly we could all have been on our way hours ago."

"Pompous little thing!" retorted the motorbike. "Who asked *you?*"

The car said that if it was all right with all the others it would be on its way.

"No need to be sarcastic," called the van as it departed.

The lorry had followed the fire engine and was already out of sight. The motorbike roared away. The bicycle went quietly about its business, and soon the road was quite deserted.

At the hospital nearby the car park was deserted. Then down the road came the motorbike. The hospital porter dismounted and hurried into the hospital. He put on his uniform and threw open the doors of the emergency entrance. "Good morning, doctor," he said as the doctor got out of the car.

"Nurse is on her way," said the doctor. "That was quite a traffic jam at the crossroads, wasn't it?" He hurried inside to put on his white coat.

"Ting-a-ling-a-ling!" said the nurse's bicycle as she rode into the car park. "I hope I'm not too late." And she followed the doctor inside.

The van came along next, and the driver jumped out. "Urgent equipment to deliver," he said to the porter.

They unloaded the van together.

"Be-bo-be-bo-be-bo!" came the cry of the ambulance as it screeched around the corner. It came to a halt beside the emergency doors and the ambulance men jumped out. "Two little children and their mother," they told the doctor and the nurse. "Caught in a fire at home, but they're not badly hurt. The fire engine got there just in time."

The lorry driver came running in. "Where are my children and my wife?" he cried. "I heard there was a fire at my home. Are they safe?"

"Quite safe," said the nurse.

On its way back to the fire station the fire engine called at the hospital. "Did we save them in time?" asked the firemen.

"Yes. Thank you," said the lorry driver. "I can't tell you how relieved I was to hear your siren at the crossroads."

"What a terrible traffic jam that was!" said the firemen.

The lorry driver shook his head in a mystified sort of way. "I can't think what was wrong with my lorry," he said. "All of a sudden it seemed to have a mind of its own."

"So did my motorbike," said the hospital porter.

"And my van," agreed the van driver.

The ambulance driver laughed. "I'm used to that," he said. "My ambulance firmly believes that it is more important than any other vehicle on the road. What do you others think?"

"Well," said the doctor, "in this case who knows whose work was most important? Let us all go home and think about it."

"After you," said the motorbike to the van.

"No, after *you*," insisted the van.

And one by one they departed in a *very* orderly fashion.

*   *   *

Follow-up Discussion

This story helps to illustrate how, in any organization, be it a hospital, school or business, every member of the team plays an integral part. This point will probably need some explanation, but it can be expanded to form a discussion about the role of the children in the situations of which they have experience, such as the family, the class and the school.

Language Development and Creative Writing

The traffic jam in the story is typical of many of our town, city and even country roads. The majority of road users have been caught up in a traffic jam, so there are probably children who will be able to discuss the situation from first-hand knowledge.

Those children who have not been involved may be encouraged to talk about sitting in a car, bus or train on a long journey.

Environmental Studies and Science

The important emergency services such as the ambulance and fire brigade are mentioned in the story. In addition, other essential services, such as electricity, water and gas, could be researched, under the heading "People who work for us".

Mathematics

Traffic counts are a feature of many school mathematical experiences. They are a very useful introduction to tallying and graphical representation.

Art and Craft
The Highway Code and Green Cross Code hold regular painting competitions to design posters to advertise their campaigns at both local and national levels.

Drama, Movement and Music
This story can be readily adapted for dramatization. The children could learn traffic songs such as the "Wheels on the Bus", "The Little Bubble Car" and "Get Out and Get Under".

The Man Who Mended Dolls

(Consideration for Others)

In days gone by there lived an old man whose name was Daniel. Daniel was shy, and very poor; he had no family, and he lived all alone in a cottage in the middle of a village.

Sometimes, when he felt lonely, he would sit outside his house in the sunshine and watch the children going by on their way to school. He never spoke to them, because he was so shy; but one day, when he was sitting by his door, a little girl came by carrying a doll. The old man saw that the doll had only one arm.

He was so sad to see it, that he forgot his shyness and said, "What happened to your doll, that she has only one arm?"

"One day I lost her," replied the child, "and when I found her again one of her arms was missing. I never could find it."

"Let me have her," said Daniel, "and when you come out of school she shall be mended and as good as new."

Because the child had heard her mother say that Daniel was a good old man, she gave the doll to him and continued on her way to school.

All that day Daniel worked hard and patiently with wood and chisel and paint, and when the child came out of school she was overjoyed to find that her doll was mended.

"How kind you are, Daniel," exclaimed the child's mother, "and how very clever! Where did you learn to mend dolls as cleverly as that?"

"I never mended a doll before," said Daniel, "but somehow I knew exactly what to do."

The next day, when Daniel was sitting in the sunshine again, another child came to him carrying a china doll. She said nothing, but held out the doll to him, and the old man was sorry to see that the doll had no eyes.

"Come back tomorrow," he said. "I will see what I can do."

He went indoors and looked in all his cupboards to see what he could find to make some eyes for the little china doll. At last, he discovered a box of beads, and among them were two bright, shiny ones, as blue as the summer sky over his cottage. "Ah, these will do!" he said to himself as he held them up to the light, and his eyes began to shine as he pictured the child's happiness when he gave her back her doll next day.

Daniel worked far into the night, making sure that the eyes were fixed firmly in the china doll's head, and he went to bed tired but happy.

The child was delighted with her doll's new eyes. She said "Thank you" to Daniel and ran off to tell her school friends about the kind old man who had mended her doll.

The years went by, and Daniel continued to mend the children's dolls. He mended wooden dolls, china dolls, teddy bears, and even toy tin soldiers. There was not a child in the village who had not brought a doll for Daniel to mend.

One day Daniel awoke to hear a knocking at the door, and when he opened it he found a group of children standing there. They looked excited, and one of them said, "Be waiting outside your door when school is over today. We have a surprise for you." Then they ran off and disappeared inside the school.

All day long Daniel wondered what the surprise could be, but he could not think of anything, and when school was over he was still as mystified as ever. The children came running out of school and across to Daniel's cottage, where he was waiting for them by his front door. "Come with us, Daniel!" they cried, and they took his hands and led him into the school. And what do you think he saw?

A long table spread with a snow-white tablecloth, and sitting around the table were all the dolls he had ever mended. It was the biggest dolls' tea party that ever had been held. "Happy birthday, Daniel!" cried the children, and they all went and stood behind the chairs where their own dolls were sitting.

"My birthday?" said Daniel in amazement. "Is it my birthday? I didn't know." For Daniel was quite alone in the world and nobody sent him presents now, or gave him cards, and for many years his birthday had gone by like any other day. The children had found it out, though, and they knew that today was a special birthday, because Daniel was eighty years old. They led him to the head of the table and brought out a cake with candles on it, and every doll had a piece of cake and a glass of lemonade.

Afterwards the children joined hands in a ring and danced

around the kind old man singing "Happy birthday to you!"
Daniel's face was bright with happiness at the kindness of the
children, and when it was time to go home, each child brought
forward a doll that the old man had mended. And he remembered
them all, and touched them gently, and thought that perhaps they,
too, remembered him.

*   *   *

Follow-up Discussion
"Talking to strangers" and "accepting lifts in cars" could be a natural
follow-up to this story. The little girl spoke to Daniel because her mother
had said he was a "good old man".

Everybody feels lonely from time to time. The children could discuss
loneliness, in particular, that of old people. Can they think of any ways
that they could help an old person who is living alone?

Language Development and Creative Writing
"My favourite toy" would make a good title for a discussion or a piece of
writing. The children could describe it in detail and say how they get
enjoyment out of playing with it. They could describe their emotions
when they have lost or broken one of their favourite toys.

Environmental Studies
A research topic into toys through the ages. How have toys changed?
What has brought about these changes? Letters could be written to toy
manufacturers who might be able to supply some information. Local
museums would also have some examples of old toys.

Art and Craft
Peg dolls are simple to make and very cheap. They could be made into
characters for a puppet theatre, which is also easy to make, using a
cardboard box.

Drama, Movement and Music
This story could be used as a play in assembly, but it also opens up
the possibility of looking at the countless stories, plays and pieces of
music which involve toys coming to life.

Mr Murphy's Gnomes

(Honesty, Consideration for Others, Tolerance)

There was a man called Mr Murphy who collected garden gnomes.
He had quite a big garden, with a pool and a fountain, a rockery,
and little paths winding among the bushes. At every turn in the
garden there stood a gnome. It seemed that Mr Murphy couldn't
get enough of them, but one thing he was most particular
about – no two of them must be alike. Mr Murphy went all over
the country looking for new garden gnomes. It was his hobby, and
a harmless one.

He was as fond of his gnomes as if they had been his children. He
gave every one a name, and when he was working in his garden he
would talk to them and pat them on the head, almost believing that
they could respond. Of course they never did, because they were
only made of plaster, but that didn't stop him.

Next door to Mr Murphy lived a man called Friddle, who was
very envious of Mr Murphy's gnomes. There was no reason why
he should be, for he had just as much money to spend as Mr Murphy
had, and there was nothing to stop him going out and buying as
many gnomes as he wanted, but Mr Friddle didn't think about that.
All he could think about was that Mr Murphy had a lot of gnomes,
while he had none, and so jealous was he that he made little holes in
his garden fence so that he could peep through and jeer at Mr
Murphy.

"How ridiculous!" he would mutter to himself when he heard
Mr Murphy talking to the gnomes. It amazed him that his
neighbour looked so happy in the company of his little friends. As
time went by he could bear it no longer. He was so angry that he
had to do something about it. One dark night, after he knew that
Mr Murphy had gone to bed, Mr Friddle crept round into Mr
Murphy's garden and picked up the first gnome he encountered.
Then he carried it back to his own garden and locked it in the
garden shed.

The following morning he saw Mr Murphy wandering about his garden looking for the missing gnome. "Anything wrong, Mr Murphy?" he called over the fence.

"One of my gnomes is missing," said Mr Murphy.

Mr Friddle pretended to be highly amused. "I expect he's run away," he said. "Gone to seek his fortune, I shouldn't wonder."

But Mr Murphy didn't laugh. He looked very sad. "Whatever has happened to him," he said, "my garden won't be the same without him. I shall miss him very much indeed."

Mr Friddle went back indoors to have a good laugh, but somehow he didn't laugh as heartily as he might have done. He couldn't forget how sad Mr Murphy had looked. "Well," he told himself, "he's a very stupid man to make so much of little bits of plaster," and he resolved that before long he would take another one.

Accordingly, one night, a week or so later, he crept round to Mr Murphy's garden and took away another gnome, which he locked in the garden shed with the first one.

Again Mr Murphy came out looking for his gnome, and again Mr Friddle asked him what was the matter.

"Another gnome has disappeared," was the reply. "My poor old Rusty, too, the very first one I ever bought."

"Fancied a change of air, I expect, after all this time," laughed Mr Friddle, but he didnt enjoy the joke as much as he had thought he would. He wondered if Mr Murphy suspected him of being the thief, but if he did, Mr Murphy never said a word about it.

One by one all Mr Murphy's gnomes were locked up in Mr Friddle's shed, but not once did Mr Murphy accuse Mr Friddle of having taken them. At last Mr Murphy told his neighbour that he had decided to start his collection all over again, for he could not live without his gnomes. One day he started out to look for a new gnome. He was away all day, and when he came back he went out into the garden and placed his new gnome beside the waterfall.

Mr Friddle looked over the fence. "Don't you think it's a little bit silly," he said angrily, "to keep buying gnomes when someone is taking them away?"

"Not at all," replied Mr Murphy, "but I know that you don't understand my fondness for them. That is why I have brought you a present back from my wanderings."

"A present!" echoed Mr Friddle. "What is it?"

Mr Murphy handed it over. "It's a plaster bird to stand in your garden," he said. "I thought *you* might like to start a collection, too."

Mr Friddle didn't know what to say. The truth was that he felt rather ashamed of himself. But he took the plaster bird and stood it in his garden. At first he thought he was just humouring Mr Murphy, but somehow he couldn't help going out into his garden every so often to look at his plaster bird, and every time he looked at it he thought how nice it looked. The last thing he did before going to bed was to give his bird a name. His name was Flapper.

In the morning Mr Murphy heard him calling over the fence.

"What is it, Mr Friddle?" he enquired.

"My bird! My bird has gone!" cried Mr Friddle, and he looked very sad.

"I know how you must feel," said Mr Murphy, "but perhaps he didn't like it here and flew back to the place where I bought him."

"You know that's nonsense," said Mr Friddle angrily.

A few minutes later Mr Murphy called out, "Mr Friddle, come and look. Your bird is in my garden. It must have flown over the fence during the night."

Mr Friddle peered over the fence, and there indeed was Flapper, standing beside Mr Murphy's pool. "Stay there," smiled Mr Murphy, "I'll hand him over to you."

Mr Friddle took Flapper in his arms and replaced him in his own garden. "You're not to fly away again," he said before he thought of what he *was* saying. Mr Murphy only smiled.

The next morning Mr Murphy was not at all surprised to find that all his gnomes were back in their old places. "I'll tell you what, Mr Friddle," he said. "I'm going out to look for another new gnome today. Perhaps you'd like to come with me? Maybe you will find another bird to add to your collection."

A great load seemed to be lifted from Mr Friddle's mind. "Yes, thank you, Mr Murphy," he said. "I think I'd like that very much indeed."

* * *

Follow-up Discussion
This story provides us with another opportunity to encourage the children to talk about their emotions. They could talk or write about the things that give them pleasure and emotional pain.

"Do as you would be done by" would be a useful expression with which to open the discussion. Talk about the idea that actions whether they be kind, unkind or thoughtless, spread like the ripples from a stone thrown into a pond.

The envy exhibited by Mr Friddle will be an emotion that the children will be able to identify with and appreciate. Mr Murphy's psychology in dealing with the situation could form the basis for discussion.

Language Development and Creative Writing
The children could talk about and write about garden gnomes and imagine what they think about as they sit in their places in the garden. This could be developed into dialogue between the gnomes.

Environmental Studies, Science, Art and Craft
A small garden that the children could cultivate could be stimulated by this story. In connection with the garden, the children could make miniature gnomes and birds to put in it.

Drama, Movement and Music
The story itself can be adapted for use as a play for assembly.

"Garden gnomes" could also become the theme for a movement lesson. It would be a variation on the game of "Statues" in which the children adopt a statue position of a garden gnome.

The subject "garden gnomes" could mystify some children, because they only appeal to a particular group of gardeners. It might be possible to borrow one or two from a local garden centre, so that the children can appreciate what they really are.

The Teddy Minders

(Tolerance)

"Sally's going on holiday tomorrow," said Emma, "and she can't take her teddies with her."

"Why not?" asked Gran.

"Her Dad says there are too many," Emma said.

"How many teddies has she got?" asked Gran.

"Three," said Emma.

"Can't she just take one?" asked Gran. "Three does seem rather a lot."

"That wouldn't be fair," said Emma.

Gran nodded. "I quite agree with you," she said. "It wouldn't be fair at all. I should have thought of that."

"Sally says they get up to all sorts of tricks when she's not there to look after them," went on Emma. "She says they run all over the place and throw things about."

"They wouldn't be allowed to do things like that in *my* house," said Gran firmly. Gran was very good at pretend games.

Emma's older brother Danny said scornfully, "Don't be stupid. You know teddies can't move about by themselves."

Gran went on calmly with what she was doing. "Can't they?" she said. "I know they couldn't when I was a child, but things have changed a lot since those days."

"Anyhow," said Emma, "Sally's been crying all day. She doesn't want to leave them all on their own."

"Then there's only one thing to be done," said Gran. "We shall have to mind them until she comes back."

Danny sniffed, but Emma said, "That's a good idea, Gran. Let's go and get them now."

Emma and Gran went through the little gate between the houses and knocked on Sally's door. When Sally opened it Gran said, "I hear you're going on holiday tomorrow and you can't take your teddies with you. Would you like us to mind them for you until you get back? Sort of teddy-minding, you know."

Sally's face lit up. "I'll go and get them," she said. When she came back she told Gran (because Emma already knew), "That's Father Bear, and that's Mother Bear, and that's Baby Bear. They don't like porridge."

"I'll remember that," said Gran. "Where do they like to sleep?"

"In a box," said Sally. "You can get one from the supermarket."

"I got one this morning," Gran said, "but it smells of soap."

"They won't mind that," said Sally.

When they got back to their own house Gran and Emma put the three teddies in the box. "I'd better have them in my room," said Gran, "in case they play up in the night."

But they didn't. They were as good as gold, and in the morning Gran came downstairs and said the teddies didn't feel like breakfast but they'd have a snack about eleven if that was all right with Emma.

"I think pretend games are silly," said Danny.

Gran gave him his cornflakes and said, "I don't mind if you think they are silly, but it's unkind to spoil other people's fun." She had hardly finished speaking when there came a knock at the door. When Emma went to open it she saw a little boy holding a rather shabby teddy. "Are you the lady who minds teddies?" he asked Gran.

Gran didn't look at all surprised. "Yes I am," she said.

"Will you look after Pong for me?" he asked. "I'm going to stay on a farm and there's a dog there that chews teddies, so Mum thought I'd better leave him behind."

"Quite right," agreed Gran. "Let me see him."

The little boy handed him over. The teddy looked as if he'd been chewed already, but he was wearing a perfectly clean pair of dungarees, so Gran said she'd take him. "He'd better go in a shoe box for the time being," she said when the little boy had gone, "and when we go to the supermarket we'll get another box for him."

Gran didn't need anything from the supermarket except a sliced loaf, and the check-out lady looked rather surprised when Gran said she wanted a box to put it in. Gran explained that she wanted it for a teddy, and the lady's face changed from cross to kind. She said it was a lovely idea, and if Gran would tell her where she lived she'd bring their teddies when they went away.

"I charge sixpence a night," said Gran firmly.

"That's quite all right," said the check-out lady. "Cheap at half the price, as they say."

The news spread around like wildfire. Three more people came that day to leave their teddies for a week or two, and the following day seven people came. By the end of the week Emma and Gran were minding thirty-two teddies and had to put them to sleep four in a box, two at either end with labels around their necks to say whose teddies they were.

Gran was very strict with them all. She told them quite plainly that she'd stand no nonsense or they'd go back to an empty house, so, teddies being the sensible creatures they are, they behaved themselves very well.

"Do you think we ought to give them hot milk at bedtime?" asked Emma one night.

"You can do as you like," said Gran, "but in my opinion they are all far too fat anyhow, so a week or two without milk won't do them any harm at all."

When the next person came with a teddy Emma told her that milk at bedtime would be a penny extra, but the little girl said that her teddy hadn't been well lately and he wasn't eating anything at all.

"I hope it's nothing catching," said Gran. "I have all these other teddies to think of. He hasn't got spots anywhere, has he?"

"No," said the little girl, "but he's got a cough."

"I'll attend to it," said Gran.

Danny hadn't said anything unkind since the first morning, but Gran noticed that he kept peeping at the teddies when he thought nobody was looking. One day a soldier came to the door. He was wearing his uniform and lots of medals. He was a general. "Do you take toy soldiers?" he enquired.

Gran was cautious. "That depends," she said. "How many have you got?"

"Quite a lot," said the general. "I play battles with them."

Gran sniffed and wriggled her shoulders. "There'll be no fighting in my house," she said. "If they come here they will have to conduct themselves respectably."

The general said that if he gave them the order to stay in their box they would stay in their box. Let there be no mistake about that.

"But why do you want to leave them if they are so obedient?" asked Emma.

The general whispered confidentially, "I am going on a secret mission, and I never know for certain when I am going to get back, so I should like to know that they are in good hands. Besides," he went on, going rather pink, "I have brought an old teddy bear that I'd like you to mind for me."

"He's only got one leg!" exclaimed Emma when she saw him.

"Lost it in an encounter with the enemy," said the general. "He got a medal in that campaign."

When the general had gone, Danny said he wouldn't mind looking after the soldiers. He took them upstairs to his room and when Gran peeped in later she saw that he was drilling them on his table.

Emma and Gran were sorry when the holiday season was over and everybody came to collect their teddies. They said that they were very grateful and they could see that they had been well-minded. It was quite a long time before the general came back. "I've decided to leave the soldiers with you indefinitely," he said to Danny, "but I'll take my old teddy. After all, it wouldn't be kind to abandon him altogether, would it?"

"No it wouldn't," said Danny. Then he caught Emma smiling a little at him and he smiled back and said, "I've got to go. It's time for the soldiers to march into battle."

*   *   *

Follow-up Discussion

This story could be introduced with a discussion about tolerance, having respect for other people's thoughts and ideas, and attempting to understand other people.

Most children, boys and girls alike, form quite close relationships with their teddy bears. To some children they become "imaginary friends", with whom they hold long, involved conversations.

Children must be made to understand that they are not alone in this. Frank discussion about the teacher's childhood memories could help them to realize that adults did just the same thing when they were young.

Language Development and Creative Writing

This is another story that links very well with other stories and pieces of music about toys that come to life. The Nutcracker, Pinocchio, Coppelia and Bagpuss are just a few examples. The children could discuss, write and act out their own story or dance routine about a toy shop after closing time.

Art and Craft
Making clothes for favourite toys could be a profitable outcome of this story. There is a proliferation of dolls on the market for both girls and boys. The wardrobes are also available, but they are of questionable quality. The children could be encouraged to collect materials and with just simple stitchery could produce clothing for their dolls at a fraction of the price they would have to pay to buy it.

Drama, Movement and Music
This is a superb story for turning into a play for use in assembly.

The movement of puppets referred to under the Language and Creative Writing heading could also be used to stimulate work in movement lessons.

The Man Who Invented Nice Words

(Politeness)

Long, long ago, when all the words we speak today were just being invented, there were no nice words at all. Nobody said anything pleasant to anybody, and life was pretty miserable, I can tell you. The men spent all their days fighting, while the women stayed at home and were terribly rude to each other. Good manners hadn't been thought of. When food was found it wasn't served up nicely or shared around – oh no – it was fallen upon by everybody and gobbled up in a most disgusting way. When people went out for a walk and they found someone blocking their path they would simply shove their way past. Consideration for others was unheard-of. You can imagine what it was like living in those days. But in a cave, living all by himself, was a clever man. He wasn't considered important; in fact, nobody bothered much about him at all because he was a dwarf. His name was Nob.

Nob used to spend his days sitting on a rock outside his cave, which was draughty and damp (that was the reason why nobody ever fought him for possession of it). He would sit there for hours at a time, with his back against a rock, just thinking. He seldom talked to anybody, because he didn't like using all the nasty words like "shove off" or "It's mine!" or "get out of my way" that were in common use at that time. But he was very good at thinking.

One day he was thinking how pleasant it would be if he didn't have to watch the dreadful fights that were going on all the time, when he saw a boy come wandering by. Nob sat quietly and watched him. The boy picked up a stone and threw it with all his might into the middle of the pond that was in front of Nob's cave. He watched the water for a minute or two and then ran off.

Nob, too, had been watching the water. He saw how the ripples widened out from the spot where the stone had fallen, and then he thought a very wonderful thought indeed. It was undoubtedly the best thought he had ever had. "If that pond were the whole wide world," he thought, "and the stone were a nice word, it would spread goodwill like the ripples on the water – maybe right to the edge of the world. I think I'll invent a nice word."

He awaited his opportunity, and one day it came. A child passed by his cave. She was nibbling a tasty morsel of something she had found, but she suddenly tired of it and threw it away right at the feet of Nob. He picked it up and said "Thank you," and began to eat.

The child stared at him for a minute or two, then she went on her way. But she didn't forget what Nob had said to her. She was very interested in the new words. The next day she passed by the cave again. This time she threw down a useful stick that she had found. "Thank you," said Nob, and he picked up the stick and put it carefully beside him.

Each time the child passed the cave she left something for Nob, and he always responded in the same way. After a while the child began to say the words herself when she was at home in her own cave.

"What is that you keep saying?" demanded her mother.

"It's what Nob the dwarf says to me when I give him something," she replied, "and I like the sound of it. I like the way Nob says it."

"So do I," said her mother, "I must tell my friends about it."

Soon the new habit began to spread from cave to cave, like the ripples on the pond. The men began to notice it. "What is this thank you that the children keep saying?" they asked.

"It's a new invention," they were told, "nice words."

"Who needs nice words?" scoffed the men.

"You do," shouted the children.

"Is that so?" jeered the men.

"Yes," shouted the children.

"Who says so?" yelled the men.

"We do," cried the children.

But because they were only children the men took no notice of them and they went on fighting until they fell down dead or exhausted.

Nob was pleased with his new invention, but he knew there was still much more to be done. He saw that when people wanted something – even if it belonged to somebody else – they simply took it, and it seemed to Nob that that wasn't the right thing to do. Of course, nobody had given it a thought until then.

One day, as he was sitting in his usual place, a boy came by. His

arms were full of fruit which he had gathered. He seemed to be
very tired, because when he came near to Nob's cave he stopped to
rest, laying the fruit on the ground beside him. He looked warily at
Nob, expecting him to snatch some of the fruit in the usual way,
but to his surprise Nob said, "Have you got some fruit to spare?"

"I suppose so," said the boy.

"Please may I have some?" asked Nob.

"Yes," said the boy.

"Thank you," said Nob.

"What was that new word you used?" asked the boy.

"Please," said Nob.

"I never heard that word before," the boy said.

"I just invented it," Nob told him.

"What a good idea," the boy said. "Why don't you invent a few
more nice words? You could invent a word for when people wish
they hadn't done something bad, or a word for when people want
to pass each other on a narrow path. You could invent all sorts of
nice words, couldn't you?"

"Indeed I could," replied Nob, "and I think I will."

So he did.

*   *   *

Follow-up Discussion
This is a story that can be used at times when basic good manners begin to
lapse. From time to time this sort of situation does arise.

With the aid of this story the children will be encouraged to discuss the
use of manners. Do the children imagine that they were invented as the
story suggests? The use of phrases like "Please", "Thank you", "Excuse
me" or "I'm sorry" does not cost a penny.

The point that is made in this story is particularly relevant today. It is
set in a way that the children should be able to understand.

Language Development and Creative Writing
Though the story is very simple, it probably hints at the basic
development of language in early man. The children could discuss how
they imagine language evolved.

Environmental Studies
The story can lead into a research topic into the "Life of the Cave Man".
This is a subject that is well-documented in published material. The Trog
Books by Ben Butterworth, published by Arnold, will accompany this
project and help to reinforce it.

Art and Craft
The children can discuss the early use of art, in the Egyptian hieroglyphics on the walls of the burial chambers, cave paintings, and the body and face paintings of native tribesmen.

Drama, Movement and Music
The story should easily adapt for use as a play for assembly.

It lends itself very well to musical activities, the children using the words in the story, and others they have chosen, as a basis for improvisation and composition, based on Carl Orff methods.

The Honky-Tonk Piano

(Loyalty, The Importance of Friendships)

Against the wall in Mr March's living room there stood an old piano. It had once been a beautiful instrument, with gleaming white keys and brass candlesticks on its front, but long ago the keys had become yellow with age and the brass candlesticks had been removed. Nobody in the house was old enough to remember the piano as it had been when it was new. Nobody could even remember where it had come from.

"We ought to get rid of that piano," said Mrs March one day. "It's terribly shabby and I'm ashamed to have it in the house."

"You're right," agreed Mr March. "We'll get a new one and sell the old one."

Mrs March laughed. "Who on earth would buy that old thing?" she asked disdainfully. "Just look at it – so old-fashioned! Look at those holes where the candlesticks used to be. See how dull the wood has become. Besides, it makes such a peculiar sound when it's played, a honky-tonk sound which is so unfashionable these days. Nobody in their right senses would dream of buying it."

"Oh I don't know," Mr March said. "Somebody might buy it for scrap. It's worth a try."

Mrs March ordered a new piano, which was delivered next day and placed in the living room beside the old one. Mrs March sat down and began to play. She hadn't played the old piano for years. There was no doubt that the new one had a lovely sound, but the old piano now looked shabbier than ever by comparison with the smart new instrument standing beside it.

Mr March asked several people if they would like to buy his honky-tonk piano, but when they came to look at it they said it was far too shabby and they would much prefer to have a brand new one like Mrs March's.

One day a scrap man came around with a lorry. "Have you got any old junk you want to dispose of?" he asked.

"Well," replied Mr March, "I have a honky-tonk piano that's cluttering up my living room. Nobody wants to buy it, so perhaps you'd better take it."

The scrap man and his assistant carried the old piano out to the lorry and they drove away. They called at many more houses that day, and in the afternoon they came to a cottage where an old lady named Mrs May lived. "Any old iron!" cried the scrap man outside her door, and when she opened it, "Have you got any old iron, any old furniture, any old clothes?"

Mrs May shook her head. "No," she said. "I once gave away one of my oldest possessions and I have regretted it ever since, so now I keep my dear old things beside me."

The scrap man said he quite understood her feelings, but what he had meant when he asked for anything old was anything she didn't want any more.

"Oh, if *that's* what you mean," said Mrs May, "you'd better come in." She led him into her sitting room. "There," she said, "how would you like to buy *that*?"

"A piano!" exclaimed the scrap man. "Do you know, that's the second one I've been offered today. Mind you, this is a much better piano than the first one. Much more modern. Why do you want to dispose of it?"

"I don't know," mused the old lady. "Years ago, when I had my dear old piano, I used to enjoy playing it so much. My children and my grandchildren used to come and visit me, and we'd all gather around and sing the good old songs. Now they don't come as often as they used to, and even when they do, they don't want to hear me play. It's a very strange thing, but my house hasn't seemed the same place since I gave away my honky-tonk piano."

The scrap man exclaimed, "That's a coincidence! The piano I have on my lorry is a honky-tonk piano. The lady who gave it to me had bought a new one."

"Oh," cried Mrs May, "how I should like to see it!"

"That's easily done," said the scrap man. "Come outside."

He led the way to his lorry, and as soon as she saw it, Mrs May clasped her hands together and cried out, "It's my very own honky-tonk piano! The one I gave away! Oh, Mr Scrap Man, take away my new piano and let me have my old one back!"

"Certainly," said the scrap man, who knew a good bargain when he saw one. He called his assistant to help him. They soon had Mrs May's new piano on the lorry and the honky-tonk piano in

Mrs May's cottage, and the scrap man drove away thinking he had done very well for himself that day.

But a bargain is a bargain in more ways than one, and Mrs May was quite sure that she had struck the better one. She knew far better than Mrs March had done how to polish up the wood, for she had learnt the secret long ago. Very soon the honky-tonk piano was gleaming as it had done when it was new. Mrs May stood back and looked at it. "Something missing," she said. "I know there's something missing." Then she remembered. "The brass candlesticks!" she exclaimed. "Now what became of them?"

She climbed up into her attic and searched for a long time, and at last she found the brass candlesticks wrapped in paper and put away in a box. When she had polished them and replaced them on the front of the old piano she lifted the lid and sat down to play. She looked at the yellow keys and chuckled to herself, "You're looking a bit yellow," she said, "but then so am I, so what does it signify?"

When her children and grandchildren came to see her they were delighted to find the honky-tonk piano back in its place. Mrs May sat down and played the old songs, and they all stood around the piano and sang them in the good old way. After that they came much more frequently to see her.

Mrs March was happy because she had a brand-new piano which all her friends admired, and the scrap man was happy because he sold Mrs May's new piano at an enormous profit; but the happiest one of all was Mrs May, for her honky-tonk piano just went on making more and more people happy as her family grew.

*   *   *

Follow-up Discussion

There are several points which this story can be used to convey. The generations have a great deal to offer each other. The elderly can impart wisdom and experience to the young, who in return can bring their freshness and innocence into the lives of the older generation.

"Make new friends but keep the old
One is silver, the other gold"

is a saying that can be introduced to the children, explained and discussed.

Things that are well-made, like the honky-tonk piano, will last and continue to give pleasure for a long time. Similarly, if we make sure that our lives are built on strong, sensible foundations, we can enjoy life and give happiness to others as we grow.

So many children show little or no respect for property, whether it is their own or belongs to others. Taking care of possessions, such as books, toys and clothes, can result in their continuing to give enjoyment for many years.

Language Development and Creative Writing
Children often have a very close affinity with their grandparents and other adults in that generation. They could be encouraged to discuss or write about why they enjoy visiting their grandparents.

Environmental Studies and Science
A historical topic based on antiques could be stimulated by this story. A museum visit would be a fruitful starting point.

A collection of old things, such as books, that belong to the elderly people in the area around the school, could be assembled and exhibited. The old people could be invited into the school to talk to the children about life in their childhood days. The writer has organized just such a situation and it resulted in a very rewarding dialogue between the generations.

Art and Craft
Drawings and paintings may be done, of antique furniture and the articles collected. Making portraits of an elderly person could be preceded by discussion of how the facial features of old people differ from the children's.

Drama, Movement and Music
This story poses several technical problems for adapting into a play. It might be found that a straight reading has more impact.

There are, however, aspects of the story that can be used in a movement lesson. The children can try to imagine how very old people walk and then walk as if they themselves were elderly.

The honky-tonk piano story could be accompanied by the song "My Grandfather's Clock".

The Great Peanut Rush

(Cheerfulness in Adversity, Teamwork)

Mr Chipscatter was a lorry driver. He drove a supermarket lorry, bringing goods from the depot to supermarkets all over the country. Mr Chipscatter was a big, fat, jolly man who was always cheerful. He never lost his temper, however much he was provoked, because he believed that whatever happened always turned out for the best.

One day he drove up to a store that sold everything from candles to cornflakes, and after he had jumped down out of his cab he went to the back of the lorry to open the big doors at the back.

The store manager came out to speak to him. "Well, Mr Chipscatter," he said, "what have you brought for me today?"

"Peanuts," replied Mr Chipscatter.

"What else?" enquired the manager.

"Nothing else," said Mr Chipscatter.

The manager was quite taken aback. "What?" he cried. "No butter, no cheese, no bags of sugar, no soap, no squeezy mops, no baby powder?"

"Just peanuts," said Mr Chipscatter.

"But I ordered eggs," said the manager, "and chocolate crocodiles, and skipping ropes. What are my customers going to say when they find I've only got peanuts?"

"I think they'll be very pleased," said Mr Chipscatter. He threw open the doors and the manager peered inside.

"Not even one teeny-weeny bag of lollipops?" he said wistfully.

"Not one," said Mr Chipscatter.

The lorry was full, from floor to ceiling, with bags of peanuts.

"It will take me a hundred years to sell all those!" cried the manager.

"No it won't," laughed Mr Chipscatter. "Just get one or two of your assistants to help me unload them and we shall see what we shall see."

The manager grumbled, but he went to get the assistants. It took a long time to unload the peanuts and stack them on the shelves in the store, but at last it was done, and Mr Chipscatter sat down outside the front door to have his lunch in the sunshine. As the customers passed him they noticed his cheerful face and jolly laugh. One of them asked what it was that made him so happy.

"Peanuts," he told her.

"In that case," she said, smiling, "I must go into the store and buy some."

She bought a large bag of peanuts, and all the way home she was smiling at the recollection of Mr Chipscatter's happy countenance. When her friends enquired what it was she was smiling about she said, "Peanuts," and went on her way.

"Peanuts!" they echoed in a mystified sort of way, but the more they thought about peanuts the more they felt they would like some, so they hurried off to the store to buy some.

Other people began to notice. "Where is everybody going in such a hurry?" they enquired.

"They're going to buy peanuts," was the answer.

Immediately, everyone began to say, "Is there a shortage of peanuts?" – "Is it the latest craze?" – "Is there a special peanut sale?"

Soon the store was full of people queueing up to buy peanuts. The manager could hardly believe his eyes. Nobody seemed to want baby powder or chocolate crocodiles or any of the other goods he had ordered. He began to feel quite pleased with himself for not sending Mr Chipscatter away with his load. He stood at the door and smiled at his customers. "Peanuts," he said. "This way for the best peanuts in town. All the peanuts you want, as many as you can carry. Finest quality. Good *day* to you, Madam!"

Towards the end of the day, when the queue for peanuts began to shorten a little, Mr Chipscatter went into the store to see if they had all been sold. "Not yet," said the manager, shaking his head, "and if I don't sell them all before closing time tonight I can't give you another order."

"Don't worry," responded Mr Chipscatter. "I'll fix it for you."

He went outside and waited until the boys and girls came out of school. Then he started to balance peanuts on the end of his nose. The children stopped to watch. "That's easy," they shouted.

"You think so?" said Mr Chipscatter. "It isn't as easy as it looks."

The children ran into the store to spend their pocket money on peanuts. When they came out they all tried to balance peanuts on the end of their noses, too, and Mr Chipscatter was quite right – it wasn't as easy as they thought. Most of the peanuts fell on the ground. But the children were having fun and they didn't mind losing their peanuts. At last, when all their money was spent, the children went home.

"How many left?" Mr Chipscatter asked the manager.

"Quite a lot," was the reply.

Mr Chipscatter told him not to worry, and went outside again. He laughed. Whilst he had been inside the store, the birds had come down to eat the peanuts which the children had dropped on the ground. "No need to worry now," Mr Chipscatter chuckled to himself. "No need to worry at all."

Before long the office workers began to pass by. "Feed the birds!" cried Mr Chipscatter. "Peanuts in the store! Peanuts for the birds!"

It was such a pleasant occupation for the office workers, after being shut up indoors all day, that they decided to buy peanuts to feed the birds.

At closing time the manager came out of the store. "All gone," he said to Mr Chipscatter. "Here is your order for tomorrow, and thank you for bringing me the peanuts today. I can't imagine why so many people wanted to buy them. It's never happened before."

Mr Chipscatter roared with laughter. "And I don't suppose it will ever happen again," he said, and he jumped into his cab and drove away.

*   *   *

Follow-up Discussion
Smiling is said to be a cure for many things. Popular songs and sayings prescribe cheerfulness for a "broken heart" and for encouraging those around us to join in.

This story should provide a starting point for discussion into the infectiousness of being cheerful. The papers and television regularly feature articles about people who cheerfully put up with serious illness or injuries. These can be used as reinforcement.

Language Development and Creative Writing
Children are amongst the most susceptible to fads and crazes. Most of them are very short-lived, such as hoola-hoops and skateboards. Mr

Chipscatter's demonstration of peanut balancing started a craze with the children leaving school which is not inconceivable. The children could discuss those crazes that come and go and those which recur, such as conkers.

Environmental Studies and Science
Feeding the birds in winter is something that should be done if we wish to see birds in our gardens and school grounds. The types of foods that we give the birds should be monitored according to the birds that are resident in the area. The children could do research into the bird populations and try to discover what the different species feed on. The shape of the beak will give the children some valuable clues.

Topic Work
There is a proliferation of shops, ranging from the little corner or village store to the huge hypermarkets, through all the shops that specialize in the goods they sell. A research project into shops and the goods they sell could be encouraged by this story.

Art and Craft
Designing a poster to promote the sale of peanuts is suggested by this story.

The stacking of goods in a supermarket could also stimulate art work.

A collage made of labels from branded goods is colourful and quite easy for the younger children with limited manipulative skills.

Drama, Movement and Music
This story can be used as a play for assembly. It also provides stimuli for movement lessons. The children could watch people queueing and they could form a queue themselves, adopting different stances.

Marna's Paper Bag

(Concern for the Environment)

One afternoon, on her way home from school, Marna threw away a paper bag. She ran home and forgot all about it, but next morning, when she walked by the spot again, the bag was still there on the ground, and there was a tin can lying next to it. She didn't worry about it, because she thought that somebody would come along and clear it away.

Whilst she was in school a man passed by the spot. He had a sweet packet in his hand. He looked around for a rubbish bin, but when he couldn't see one, he threw down the sweet packet beside the can and the paper bag. "The street cleaner will sweep it up," he said to himself, and went on his way.

During the course of the day two ladies got off the bus at the corner of the street. As they walked past the spot where the little heap of rubbish was lying, they threw down their bus tickets and continued along the street without giving them another thought. And so it went on. When Marna came out of school that afternoon, there was quite a large heap of litter lying where she had thrown down the paper bag. She wondered for a moment why the man who swept the street hadn't been along that day, but she had other things to do, so off she ran without thinking any more about it.

It so happened that the man who swept the streets was ill, and no replacement could be found for him, so the street remained unswept for several days. Everyone who passed the spot deposited something, thinking that it must be the place where the street-sweeper had brushed the litter into one neat pile.

At the end of the week a man who was tidying his garden began to look for a place to throw down his garden waste. "It's much too far to take it to the dump," he said to his wife.

"Then why don't you take it down the street," she responded. "There's a place down there where everybody seems to be leaving their rubbish. I daresay the man will be along soon to collect it."

So the gardening man wheeled his wheelbarrow down the street and deposited his rubbish on the heap. Then he went back to his nice tidy garden, quite pleased with himself. His neighbour had seen what had happened. "That would be a good place to take all the building rubble I have lying around my house," he said. "I'll borrow the wheelbarrow and take it now." He had to make several trips to the heap, but his house was looking so neat and tidy that he didn't mind that.

All the people in the street began to notice what was happening. They could not resist the temptation to dump all their rubbish on the convenient heap, and at the end of the month there were old mattresses, buckets with holes in them, piles of old clothes, chairs with the stuffing sticking out of them, and lots more. Somebody pushed along an old motor car and left it there, blocking the street and causing a traffic jam. Nobody could walk along the street now, and Marna couldn't get to school.

"Why doesn't somebody come along and clear up the rubbish?" the people began to say to each other. "It's quite disgraceful leaving it there. It's beginning to smell."

And so it was. The people who lived in the street had to keep all their doors and windows tightly shut, and when they went out to catch the bus at the end of the street, they had to pinch their noses between their fingers and thumbs.

One day it started to rain. All day the rain poured down out of a heavy black sky. The heap of rubbish was lying on top of the drain, so the water could not run away. The houses were flooded. The shops were flooded. The school was flooded. "Will somebody go and complain to the authorities!" screamed the people. "Get the police and the fire brigade! Do something!"

Marna watched, and listened, but said nothing. She thought about her paper bag. She knew that it was her paper bag that had started it all.

The street-sweeper heard what had happened, and he sent a message to the people who lived in the street: "Every one of you must take away the rubbish that you left there."

At first the people were offended. "We'll do no such thing!" they cried. "Other people left their rubbish there, too. Why shouldn't we?" But as the rain got heavier and the water crept higher, they knew they had to do something. They waded through the water and began to take away their own rubbish. Soon the drain was cleared. The water began to flow away. The rain stopped, and the sun came out. Marna ran out of her house. Only a few scraps of soggy paper were left in the street, but Marna knew that they were all that remained of her paper bag. She picked them up as best she could. "I'll never throw anything down in the street again," she said to herself. And she never did; nor did any of the people who lived in that street, and anyone will tell you that Marna's street, to this very day, is the cleanest one you could ever wish to find.

*   *   *

Follow-up Discussion

This story helps to illustrate how litter accumulates. The children can be encouraged to think about and discuss the health and safety hazards that are caused by the careless disposal of rubbish. For example, throwing bottles into rivers, streams and ponds can cause subsequent injury to people paddling.

The "Keep Britain Tidy" campaign is one that needs to be constantly reinforced and this story helps to do just that.

Discussion can be skilfully guided into complying with the Country Code, taking litter home and having respect for others, whether they be people or animals.

Language Development and Creative Writing

The majority of children love animals and dislike the idea of their being hurt in any way. If they are put into a situation where they think that a careless or thoughtless act on their part would cause an animal to be injured, they might show more responsibility in disposing of litter. This situation could form the basis for a fruitful language development or creative writing lesson.

Environmental Studies and Science

People who work for us to dispose of refuse; recycling waste products; and the sewage system are just some of the themes which could be developed into profitable topics.

Art and Craft

Designing a poster to draw people's attention to the problems of litter is a natural progression from this story. The "Keep Britain Tidy" groups throughout the country regularly organize competitions on this theme. This story, with well-managed follow-up, might result in a prize-winning entry.

Drama, Movement and Music

This story can be adapted for use as a play in school assembly, but the moral might be brought home more forcibly by reading the story to the school, when litter in the playground has become a problem.

The children could compose a jingle to accompany a play based on litter. This could be submitted to your local "Keep Britain Tidy" group, for use in a television campaign.

Katinka, the Poor Princess

*(Consideration for Others, Loyalty,
Concern for the Environment)*

Long ago there lived a king who was as rich as rich could be. In fact, he was so rich that even his toothbrush was made of gold, and he ate diamonds and rubies for breakfast – with milk and sugar, of course. But there came a time when the king lost all his wealth, and because he couldn't live without his riches, he died, leaving behind his only daughter, the Princess Katinka.

Katinka was very young, and because there was no-one else who wanted her now that she was poor, she went to live with her old nurse in a cottage in the hills. There she grew up like any other poor girl, learning to weave and sew and how to use the herbs that grew in the hills and woods around. She didn't mind in the least being poor. She would sing all day and laugh with her nurse about the ridiculous things her father had done when he had been so rich.

She made friends with all the people who lived among the hills, and they loved her so much for her good humour and lack of conceit, that in every home she visited she was treated like one of the family. Some of the older people used to tease her about being a princess, but it was all in fun. "Come in, Your Royal Highness," one old man would say with a chuckle, "but don't sit on my satin cushions in case you crumple them, and don't drink from my silver goblet in case you are tempted to take a bite out of it!" And Princess Katinka would laugh with the old man, because she knew that he had never seen a satin cushion or owned a silver goblet in his life.

Her best friend of all was a young shepherd called Kell, with whom she would scramble about the hillsides after the sheep, and play with the sheep-dog's puppies (who knew, with the wisdom of all animals, that she was a true friend to them).

Kell would make crowns for Katinka, from wild flowers and leaves that he gathered in the hedgerows, and would pretend to crown her Queen of the Sheep. Then they would dance through the village whilst the people cheered and cried "Long Live Queen Katinka!" And Katinka, full of fun, would call some of them to her and touch them on their shoulders with a shepherd's crook as they bowed their knees before her.

"Arise, Sir Benjamin!" she said to the old man with whom she had joked about the satin cushions and the silver goblet. "You shall be my Lord Chamberlain and keep the keys of my palace in your pocket!" – which made the old man as pleased as any Lord Chamberlain ever had been.

"And what shall I be?" asked Kell, who secretly loved Katinka more than all the gentle sheep in the world, and all his green pastures, and all the flowers that bloomed in summer.

"You are my prince," replied Katinka softly, "and always shall be," and that pleased the young shepherd and made him hope that one day Katinka might consent to be his wife.

But one day, when Katinka was helping her nurse to clean the cottage where they lived, there came a messenger from the city, and when he saw Katinka he fell on his knees before her. "Madam," he cried, "I come to tell you that your father's lands and riches are all restored and that your people wish you to return and be their Queen."

"Why should I return?" responded the princess. "I am happy living here."

"It is your duty, Madam," said the messenger. "You are the rightful heir. You must be loyal to your people."

Katinka felt no joy at the thought of becoming a Queen. She went out walking, all alone, and looked at all the places where she had been so happy. But her duty was clear and she knew that she must go. She returned to the messenger and told him that she would return.

It was a triumphant day when Katinka came back to her palace. The city was thronged with people waving and cheering on their beautiful Queen. She was dressed in robes of silver and gold, and rode in a coach drawn by six white horses. The crown upon her head sparkled with a thousand jewels. Yet that evening, in the palace gardens, she was not happy. Her ladies-in-waiting told her that she must not take off her shoes and run barefoot in the grass, and her new Lord Chamberlain, who was haughty and proud, didn't know how to smile, and wanted her to walk through the palace with her nose in the air.

Soon there came kings and princes to ask for her hand in marriage, but Katinka said to each one of them in turn, "How fare the sheep in your country?"

"Sheep, Madam?" said the kings and princes in surprise. "We are kings and princes. We do not look at sheep."

"How do the wild flowers grow?" she went on dreamily.

"Wild flowers are not for us," said the kings and princes. "Our gardens are full of orchids and lilies."

Katinka sent them away, and the kings and princes said, "Queen Katinka is very strange. She talks about sheep and wild flowers, and she refuses to accept any one of us in marriage." And because they were angry with her for rejecting them, they began to say, "She would do better to marry a shepherd and live among sheep – and serve her right!"

At length, these words came to the ears of the young shepherd Kell, and he knew at once that Katinka had kept a secret in her heart, too. So he went to the palace and demanded to see her. "Tell her," he said, "that her true prince has come."

When Katinka saw Kell, she ran down from her throne and threw her arms about his neck and kissed him. "Take me home," she begged. "This palace is no place for me. I am not happy here."

Kell was leading her away when the Lord Chamberlain cried, "But, Madam, you are our Queen! Must I remind you of your duty?"

Katinka hesitated, and suddenly she knew what she must do.

"I am still your queen," she told the Lord Chamberlain, "but the hills shall be my palace, Sir Benjamin shall be my Lord Chamberlain, my friends at home shall be my ministers, for they are wise, and kind, and good."

So Katinka and Kell went home to the hills, and the old Lord Chamberlain ran protesting all the way behind their carriage. But when he met the new Lord Chamberlain, Sir Benjamin, they soon became the best of friends, and together they helped Katinka to teach her people the gentle ways she had learnt of them. Of course, she and Kell were married, and he gave her a new-born lamb for her wedding present.

*   *   *

Follow-up Discussion
There are several potentially fruitful discussion points which this story could promote.

Katinka's preference for the simple things in the hills, rather than the riches and position of power she inherited, can be developed into a discussion about enjoyment of the environment.

The loyalty shown by Katinka for Kell and Benjamin, and by them for her, could make a good starting point for discussion.

Language Development and Creative Writing
Happiness is something that cannot be bought. Katinka found happiness in the mountains. The children could think about, talk about and write about the things that make them happy.

Environmental Studies and Science
The story opens up three possible avenues in environmental studies and science, the first being the Flora and Fauna in the hills. The second is Sheep, Shepherds and Sheepdogs, which could be run either on its own or in conjunction with number one. The third topic is Gold and Precious Stones.

Art and Craft
The children could do simple weaving on wooden or cardboard frames.

Drama, Movement and Music
This is a delightful story for adaptation into a play for use in assembly.

The children could be encouraged to make up the kind of dances they imagine Katinka and Kell would do through the streets.

Mrs Tippett and the Yellow Blanket

(Cheerfulness in Adversity)

Mrs Tippett was a home help. She went to a different house to help with the housework every day except Sunday, when she went to church in a large blue hat.

Mrs Tippett loved housework. She loved to dust and to sweep and to wash clothes. She didn't mind looking after babies, either. Everybody said that Mrs Tippett was a lovely, cheerful, pleasant lady to have about the house, and so she was.

The lady whom she helped on Mondays was called Mrs Pottlewell. Mrs Pottlewell lived at the top of the hill. Every Monday morning Mrs Tippett would climb the hill, singing a happy song, and when she arrived at Mrs Pottlewell's house the first thing she always did was to say "Good morning" to the grandfather clock. Mrs Tippett was always talking to things, and she didn't mind in the least that they couldn't answer her. "I'm going to give you a lovely polish today," she would say to a table. "That will make you feel better, won't it?" And in this way Mrs Tippett passed her days.

One Monday morning she climbed the hill as usual, entered Mrs Pottlewell's house, and said "Good morning" to the grandfather clock.

"Is that you, Mrs Tippett?" called out Mrs Pottlewell, who wasn't a strong lady, and who had to spend most of her days lying on a sofa.

"Yes it is, Mrs Pottlewell," replied Mrs Tippett, going in to see her, "and a very good morning to you. The sun is shining, the wind is blowing, and it is a perfectly beautiful washing day."

"Will you wash my yellow blanket today, please, Mrs Tippett?" asked Mrs Pottlewell.

"Of course I will," said Mrs Tippett. She took the yellow blanket into the kitchen. "Now would you prefer to go into the washing machine, or shall I put you in the sink and diddle you up and down?"

"Are you speaking to me, Mrs Tippett?" enquired Mrs Pottlewell, "because if you are, I think I should prefer to be diddled up and down in the sink."

"I'm talking to the yellow blanket, Mrs Pottlewell!" laughed Mrs Tippett.

"What a treasure you are, Mrs Tippett," said Mrs Pottlewell. "Always so cheerful, whatever happens."

"I hope I am," said Mrs Tippett.

She put the yellow blanket into the sink and diddled it up and down in the soapy water. Then she rinsed it and wrung it out and took it outside to the washing line. "I won't put the pegs on too tightly," she said, "in case they pinch you."

When she went back indoors she noticed that the children had spilt honey on the kitchen floor. "You will have to be scrubbed," she said to the floor, "and I hope you don't object to the big red scrubbing brush, because that's what I'm going to use on you."

"Are you speaking to me, Mrs Tippett?" called Mrs Pottlewell.

"Not this time, dear," said Mrs Tippett, and she sang as she started to scrub.

"Always so cheerful," murmured Mrs Pottlewell.

When Mrs Tippett had finished scrubbing the kitchen floor she noticed that the children had spread sticky finger-marks all over the table. She didn't feel cross, because she knew that children *will* do these things, and she set to work. "I'm going to spread you all over with lovely polish," she said, "and then I'm going to rub you with a soft flannel until you're as shiny as a brass button. Then I shall put a vase of daffodils on top of you."

"Are you speaking to me, Mrs Tippett?" asked Mrs Pottlewell.

"Not this time, dear," replied Mrs Tippett as she polished away.

When she had finished that job, Mrs Tippett went to look for another. Suddenly Mrs Pottlewell called out, "Oh, Mrs Tippett – look at that! The yellow blanket has come off the line, and is blowing away!"

Mrs Tippett ran out of the house. She couldn't help smiling at the way the yellow blanket was whirling around in the air, and she cried, "Oh, you rascal! Come back at once! Mrs Pottlewell needs you."

But the yellow blanket was flying high in the air, right over the top of the house. Mrs Tippett ran out into the street, and followed the blanket right down the middle of the village. The village children thought it was great fun to see Mrs Tippett chasing after the blanket, so they followed her. Down the main street, behind the shops, through the churchyard, and into the meadows they went, and all the time Mrs Tippett was calling to the yellow blanket to come back, with the children echoing everything she said. She knew how funny she must look, and she laughed as she ran. She knew it wouldn't help at all to lose her temper.

At last she had to pause for breath beneath a great old tree. "Can you help me, tree?" she pleaded. "Next time the yellow blanket blows near you will you catch it for me?"

"Mrs Tippett is talking to the tree!" laughed the children as they danced around her. Mrs Tippett only smiled back at them and mopped her brow with her apron.

But then a strange thing happened. As the yellow blanket flew over the tree one of its branches seemed to move upwards, and before the blanket could evade its grasp it was caught and held.

Mrs Tippett clapped her hands. "Thank you, tree," she said. "Now will you please drop it just here?"

And the tree dropped the yellow blanket right into Mrs Tippett's arms, where it lay as good as gold. The children helped Mrs Tippett to fold it. "Quite dry," she smiled, "and ready to be used again."

She waved goodbye to the children and went back to Mrs Pottlewell's house. "I'm going to wrap you up in a nice warm yellow blanket," she said, "and then I'm going to make you a nice cup of tea."

"Are you speaking to me, Mrs Tippett?" enquired Mrs Pottlewell.

And this time, of course, she was.

*   *   *

Follow-up Discussion
This story could be used in connection with a topic on "People Who Help". A home help or home help organizer might be persuaded to come into school to talk about their duties.

The discussion that follows this story could be steered round to include all the people who help others that the children can think of. They can think about and debate ways in which they can help others and, in particular, old people.

Language Development and Creative Writing
The older children could continue the discussion of jobs. It could develop into a discussion about the types of jobs the children would like to do when they grow up.

What do the children expect to get from a job of work? Can they foresee any disadvantages or difficulties that they might experience in their job?

Environmental Studies and Science
Drying clothes could be researched. What are the best conditions for drying? How long does it take for clothes to dry under different conditions? Why do clothes dry better when it is windy?

Art and Craft
The yellow blanket on the washing line or being blown away by the wind would make a subject for a painting lesson.

Drama, Movement and Music
"Mrs Tippett and the Yellow Blanket" will make a good play for use in assembly.

CHAPTER TWO

Weather and the Seasons

Mrs Greenfinger

(Caring and Sharing, Concern for the Environment)

Once upon a time there was a large family. There was Mr Smith, who made shoes for horses, and Mrs Smith who was a lace-maker, and twelve children.

Each one of the children had a favourite occupation. Billy was good at baking, and Bobby was clever at making clothes. Jenny painted pictures to hang on the walls. Bella made patchwork quilts, Johnny carved toys from wood, Francis invented games. The twins, Emmie and Stephen, were clever carpenters who could make all the tables, chairs and beds that the family needed. Jim enjoyed cleaning the house, Jemima made pots, and little Silas was very good at weaving. So between them all they got on very well, and their house was as comfortable as could be. Yes, I know what you want to say: if there was Billy, and Bobby, and Jenny and Bella, Johnny, Francis, the twins, Jim, Jemima, and Silas, who was the twelfth?

Well, the twelfth child was Septimus, a big, clumsy, awkward lad, who had tried his hand at everything about the house without success.

"You must try harder, Septimus," his mother scolded him one day. "There must be something you can do. Go and help one of your sisters or one of your brothers. I'm sure that if you really try you will succeed at something."

So Septimus went to help Billy with the baking. He loved kneading and slapping the dough and shaping it into loaves, but somehow it never seemed to turn out the way it should. He got the dough in his hair, and the jam in his ears, and he dropped the pudding on the kitchen floor. "Oh, go away, Septimus!" cried Billy. "You're nothing but a nuisance. I can get on better without you."

Septimus, who really had been trying very hard, went away feeling hurt by his brother's unkind words, though he said nothing in reply. When he was feeling a little better he went to Jemima and pleaded with her to let him help her. "I'd like to make a pot to cook potatoes in," he said.

"Oh, Septimus," sighed Jemima, "what kind of a pot can you make with your clumsy hands?"

"Just let me try," begged Septimus.

Jemima stood aside and watched him as he threw the clay on to the potter's wheel, but before long it flew in all directions, and as Jemima scraped up the clay from the floor she said, "I knew you'd make a mess of it. Why don't you go and help somebody else instead?"

Septimus crept away into a corner, where he sat for a long time until his father came by and told him that he ought to be ashamed of himself, idling his time away when the rest of the family were all so busy doing things to benefit each other. "Go and see if you can be of any assistance to your brother Bobby," he said.

"Help me!" laughed Bobby. "Can't you see what I'm doing? I'm making dye to colour the wool that Silas is going to weave into a coat for Jenny. Now you know what happened the last time you helped me to make dye. You dyed yourself up to the elbows in purple and you couldn't get it off for weeks and weeks. Oh no, Septimus, I can't allow that to happen again. Just leave me alone, there's a good fellow."

And so it went on. Septimus tried to help each of his brothers and sisters in turn, but by the end of the day he still hadn't done anything right. He had tried to make a bed, but it had collapsed under the weight of little Emmie. He had tried to do some weaving, but somehow the weft had run away with him and he had so completely tied up his poor brother Silas that it had taken hours to unwind him again.

"You're no good for anything," cried his brothers in exasperation, and they pushed him out of the house and locked the door so that he couldn't get in to do any more damage. Septimus went sadly away.

He always felt happier out of doors, and he was such a good-natured youth that before long he had quite forgiven his brothers and sisters for their harsh words. He went into the field behind the house and sat down in the grass to think. After a while he said aloud to himself. "Everybody is good at something. The only difficulty is finding out what that something is, but I have no doubt I shall think of it before long." He thought and thought, but all that came to him was the feeling that being out of doors was the best occupation in the world and that the smell of growing things was far nicer than the smell of baking bread, or paint, or clay.

Suddenly he noticed that he was not alone. A lady was sitting close beside him. And what a strange lady she was! She was entirely green from head to foot. Not just her clothes, but her skin and her eyes and her hair – even her lips were green. Septimus blinked and rubbed his eyes. He closed them for a moment, but when he opened them again the lady was still there.

"Well, Septimus," she said cheerfully, "you haven't had much success today, have you?"

"I never do," he replied. "It's my hands, you see. Did you ever see such big, clumsy things in all your life? Can you wonder that I can't do anything properly?"

The lady took his hands in hers, and when she had looked at them for a time she said, "I see nothing wrong with them, and I think I can say that I am something of an expert on hands."

"Who are you?" asked Septimus.

"My name is Mrs Greenfinger," she said, "and I have come to help you."

Septimus laughed. "Perhaps you are my fairy godmother," he said.

"Perhaps I am," she responded, "but it's best not to laugh about things like that."

"Can you really help me?" Septimus asked her.

"Oh I think so," she replied. "Tell me, Septimus, what do you like doing more than anything else in the world?"

"I like being out here," he said. "I'm too clumsy indoors. But as to doing anything, why, I don't know what it could be."

Mrs Greenfinger smiled and stood up. "I think you will know before long," she said. "I have put an idea into your head. Don't worry any more, Septimus, your troubles are all over." And as he looked at her she seemed no more than a cloud against the setting sun. He put his hand in front of his eyes to shade them from the glow, but as he did so Mrs Greenfinger vanished.

Septimus lowered his hand, and as he did so he caught sight of his fingers. He looked at the other hand, and gasped with astonishment. Where Mrs Greenfinger had touched him he was green. He took out his pocket handkerchief and tried to rub it off. He ran to the stream and plunged his hands into the water, but however hard he rubbed, the colour would not come off. "What shall I do?" he groaned. "I'm in trouble enough already. What will my brothers and sisters say when they see this?" – and he flung himself down in the grass.

He stayed there until the sun had set. It was too dark now to see his hands, so he went back home. The family were all in bed, having unlocked the door for him and left his supper on the table, for they were by no means cruel to him, for all his clumsiness. After he had eaten his supper he climbed into bed and fell into a deep sleep.

The first thing he thought about in the morning was Mrs Greenfinger. He pulled his hands out from underneath the bedclothes, and to his utter dismay he saw that his fingers were still quite green. He groaned aloud.

"What is the matter, Septimus?" cried his brothers, crowding round his bed. "Are you ill?"

"No," he said, "but look at my fingers."

"What's the matter with them?" asked Bobby.

"Can't you see it?" cried Septimus. "Can't you see how green they are?"

"No," said his brothers, shaking their heads.

Septimus went downstairs. His sisters and his mother were in the kitchen. "Can you see my green fingers?" he asked, holding them up.

"Don't be silly, Septimus," laughed Emmie. "They're as brown as ever they were."

Septimus sought out his father, who had been working in the forge since early light. "Father," he said, "I don't know how it is, but yesterday, when I was in the field, I thought my fingers had turned green, and I can see it still. Mother can't see it, nor can my brothers and sisters, so I want you to look at them."

"Green fingers?" said his father, stopping to look. "I wish you had."

"Why, Father?" asked Septimus. "What do you mean?"

"I mean this," was the reply, "that if you had green fingers you could grow all the vegetables and fruit that such a large family needs and then, perhaps, we shouldn't have to work so hard."

And suddenly Septimus understood. He had heard, long ago, of the old saying that anyone who was good at growing things was possessed of green fingers. He laughed out loud. That was the one thing he had never tried to do. That was what Mrs Greenfinger had meant when she said she had put an idea into his head. He loved to be out of doors. He loved the smell of growing things. He felt far less clumsy in the open. He would be a gardener.

He took a spade and began to dig. He found that he was very good at it. The rows were deep and straight, and his strong hands and heavy frame seemed exactly suited to the work he was doing. Never had he felt happier. Before the sun went down that night he had planted seeds, fruit bushes, and nut trees. He had been in nobody's way and had quite enjoyed the solitude of his occupation.

Weeks went by. Every day Septimus worked in his garden. Green shoots came out of the ground. Leaves appeared on the bushes and trees. It was as if everything he touched prospered. Every day he was able to take something indoors for the family to eat. And what a harvest of fruit there was to make into jam and preserves! What bags of nuts to put in store for the winter! Septimus had found his true occupation at last.

To the end of his days Septimus was a gardener, but he never told a soul about Mrs Greenfinger, and he stopped asking people if they could see his green fingers. Sometimes, just as the sun was going down, he fancied that he caught a glimpse of the skirts of Mrs Greenfinger, but whenever he turned to look her full in the face she had gone.

*   *   *

Follow-up Discussion
The caring and sharing theme is very well highlighted in this story but, in addition, Septimus shows his enjoyment of the environment and that being cheerful helps one to cope with hardships.

The children may need some guidance to enable them to grasp the last two points, but they are just as important as the former. Many children will appreciate Septimus's clumsy and often amusing attempts to help.

Some children will probably associate with Septimus, because this is one of those periods in their development when clumsiness seems to be a hallmark.

Most schools, possibly every class, has a child in it who only needs to look at the water pots for them to fall over, depositing their contents over all the paintings in the near vicinity.

It is these children who feel most insecure during this stage in their development. They also have difficulty in performing physical activities. This story, with a sympathetic follow-up discussion, could help to restore some confidence, if all the children realize that the ungainly child can succeed in other areas of the curriculum.

Language Development and Creative Writing
Listening to other children talking about their feelings when they have
been involved in an unfortunate accident in the classroom can help others
to appreciate that accidents will happen.

Environmental Studies and Science
"Mrs Greenfinger" could be developed into a study of growing things.
Many scientific and observational skills can be exercised through this
project.

Mathematics
In connection with the project on growing things, the opportunities for
measuring, timing, weighing and the pictorial representation of the data
collected provide some rewarding work in mathematics.

Art and Craft
The story provides the stimulus for the children to do work with clay,
wood and other art and craft media. The children could also do paintings
of how they imagine Septimus's garden to look.

Drama and Movement
This story will adapt well for use as a play in assembly.
   There are also aspects of the story that can be used in a movement and
mime lesson. Plants growing and flowers opening can provide the stimuli
for mime or dance themes.

Mr Brown and His Interesting Dog

(Caring and Sharing, Teamwork)

Mr Brown was a nice man who owned an interesting dog. His dog was interesting for several reasons. He was short and square, he had a very broad back, and four bow legs, one on each corner, so that he looked rather like an old-fashioned sofa. His name was Chippendale. Chippendale was very fond of children, and children loved him, too.

Mr Brown was quite interesting, too. He didn't look like a sofa, but he also was short and square, with a broad back and bow legs, although he only had two.

One day Mr Brown was walking on the common with Chippendale when the north wind came along and looked down at them. "Oho!" he chuckled, "here's an interesting pair to play with. How can they stand upright on those funny bow legs? I think I'll give them a bit of a blow and see if they can keep their feet." So he blew quite hard, but he didn't blow Mr Brown and Chippendale over; in fact, they quite enjoyed it.

"Great fun, Chippendale, old chap," laughed Mr Brown. "I do like a good blow now and then, don't you?"

Chippendale ran back and forth on his funny bow legs and looked more interesting than ever.

The north wind blew harder. He was sure that he could blow them over, but however hard he tried, he couldn't do it. Soon he became rather annoyed, and he went to fetch his wife, the east wind, to help him. They both began to blow together.

"Better than ever!" cried Mr Brown. "How exhilarated I am! How the blood rushes into my cheeks and makes my eyes sparkle! Oh, there's nothing I enjoy more than a good north-easter!"

Chippendale ran in circles around his master. Being so nicely balanced, with a leg on each corner, he didn't care a bit for the winds.

Now the two winds really began to get angry. They had almost worn themselves out trying to blow Mr Brown and Chippendale over, but the two of them seemed as lively as ever. The east wind went off into the clouds and brought back their children, and showed them the man and the dog whom they were trying to blow over. "Ready, steady, go!" cried the north wind, and they all blew as hard as they possibly could.

"Blow them into the pond!" shrieked the little winds. "Blow hard, hard, harder!"

Although Mr Brown and Chippendale remained on their feet, they soon found themselves being blown towards the pond, which was cold and black.

"We're doing it, we're doing it!" screamed the little winds. "What fun! Blow harder, Mother. Blow harder, Father! What a fine splash they will make when they go into the pond!"

Now all this time the gentle south wind had been watching what was happening, and when she saw the danger that Mr Brown and his dog were in, she hurried away to find her husband, the west wind, who was busy blowing rain clouds over the mountains. When she had explained to him what was going on, the west wind gathered their children together and they all crept up on the north wind and his family and tried to blow them back to the cold north regions where they lived.

It was no use. The north wind and his family were far too strong for the west wind and his family. Mr Brown and Chippendale were blown first one way and then another, but always getting nearer to the cold, black pond.

And it was then that Chippendale showed what an interesting dog he really was, for he barked a message to all the children he had ever met. He barked in the direction of his left foreleg, and in the direction of his right foreleg; in the direction of his left hindleg and the direction of his right hindleg. This is what he said: "Children, children, come and help! My master is in trouble. Come and help the south wind and all her family to blow the north wind and his family away!"

And do you think the children heard him? Of course they did. They came running from all directions, and when they arrived on the common they began to blow. They blew with all their might. First one of the little north-east winds was blown away, and then another, and another. At last the east wind was carried away before the combined breath of the children, and she was closely followed by the north wind. Soon they had gone so far away that there was not a sign of them.

The south wind gathered her children together, and they all went off to help the west wind blow the rain clouds over the mountains. The children made a great fuss of Chippendale, and Mr Brown thanked the children for their help and invited them all home to tea.

*   *   *

Follow-up Discussion
All the children will have had experience of the wind and will be able to discuss what it feels like to walk into a strong wind or with the wind blowing behind them. Many of them will be able to recall having something blown away by the wind.

Teamwork is an important aspect in overcoming any adversity. Most young children seldom experience this until they start school. This is the first time they have had to cope with a situation where there are lots of children competing for a toy or attention.

The story helps to illustrate the point that the combined effort of good will always triumph over evil.

Language Development and Creative Writing
The children can discuss words which are used to describe the wind, such as breeze, gale, gusty. Onomatopoeic words that describe the sound of the wind could also be discussed.

Environmental Studies and Science
This is a very appropriate story for use in connection with a study of the weather and, in particular, winds. The Beaufort Wind Scale can be introduced and simple wind speed and direction indicators made.

The different ways in which the wind is harnessed, to turn a windmill, to power a sailing boat and by a farmer to scatter seeds, is another area of study that can be explored.

"Chippendale looked like an old-fashioned sofa". The older children could do some research into great British craftsmen and inventors such as Chippendale, Wedgwood and Macadam. Each area of the country had its own highly-skilled local craftsmen in furniture, pottery, silversmithing and clockmaking. A local study into local craftsmen could be profitable.

Mathematics
Work on the major points of the compass can be done, along with work on the degrees of a circle, and right angles.

Art
Paintings of Chippendale and other funny animals could prove rather amusing.

Drama and Movement
"Mr Brown and His Interesting Dog" is a story that is easily adaptable for use as a play in assembly.

There are aspects of the story that can be used in a movement and mime lesson – for instance, standing and walking with the wind blowing into the face or behind.

The Balloon Man

(Honesty)

In a small but beautiful country there lived a man who sold balloons for a living. His name was Adolphus. Every morning Adolphus would go to the cathedral square where the tourists came to look around, and there, by the fountain, he would blow up his balloons and tuck the strings into his belt to prevent them from floating away.

"Balloons!" he would cry. "Beautiful balloons! Come and buy my beautiful balloons. Any colour. Take your pick. Come and buy!" And people did buy his balloons, because they were pretty and cheap, for people love to have a bargain on a summer's day when they are on holiday. Adolphus did not become rich from the balloons he sold, but he always had sufficient money at the end of every day to have a good meal in the café on the corner. He was content.

One day, however, just when Adolphus had blown up all his balloons and attached them to his belt, a strong wind began to blow. It was the strongest wind he could ever remember. The people who would have bought balloons did not venture out into the middle of the square, but kept to the shelter of the buildings. It was in vain that Adolphus cried, "Come and buy!" for nobody would come near him.

"What a silly man," the tourists said, "to sit out there crying 'Balloons', when nobody dares venture out into the square for fear of being blown over." They called to Adolphus to leave his post. The café proprietor invited him to go and have a cup of coffee, but Adolphus had not sold even one balloon, so he stayed where he was. He kept hoping that the wind would drop as quickly as it had sprung up. He held on to the stone pillar beside the fountain and waited.

The wind blew stronger; it tugged at the balloons and made them dance like wild things around his waist. It pulled and tugged at the strings, until Adolphus found himself having to cling to the pillar with both hands. "If only someone would come along and buy my balloons," he thought, "I could run for the shelter of the buildings and be safe. Perhaps someone is having a party today and they will come and buy all my balloons together."

In the shadow of a nearby doorway, a little girl named Maria was crouching. She had been given money to buy a balloon, but when the wind had started to blow so hard, she had been afraid to run into the centre of the square. She waited, watching Adolphus with anxious eyes as he clung to the pillar.

Suddenly, a great gust swept across the square. It was too strong for Adolphus and he could hold on no longer. He found himself being tugged backwards by the wind. In a moment the wind seized hold of the balloons and swept them up into the sky – and poor Adolphus with them.

"Let go, you foolish man!" cried the people, not realizing that Adolphus was so securely attached to his balloons. "Let go, before you fly any higher!"

Adolphus could not hear them for the roaring of the wind. Up and up he went, over the shops and the houses and the great, grey towers of the cathedral; and round and round he went in a huge spiral, so that the people watching down below became dizzy at the spectacle. Adolphus was very frightened. He could see the square, and the fountain where he had been sitting but a little while before, but now they looked so tiny that he had to shut his eyes to keep out the sight.

After a few moments, he knew what he must do. He must release the balloons one by one, so that he would drop gradually down to the ground. He could have wept at the thought. His balloons, his beautiful balloons, his only means of livelihood – they would all be swept away by the wind and he would have nothing to eat that day. But he saw no help for it. If the wind continued to sweep him away from the town, he would have a long walk back and possibly not arrive home until the end of the week. He would be very hungry by then.

He waited until the wind had swept him around in a full circle and he was back over the town square. Then he started to untie the balloons, one by one. As each one floated away, he fell a little lower, until the last one was released and he dropped back into the square. Apart from having lost all his balloons, he was very little the worse for his experience.

Within a few moments the wind dropped, until it was safe for little Maria to come running over to him. "You want to buy a balloon?" said Adolphus with a rueful smile. "I'm afraid you will have to catch one first."

"I will," cried Maria, and off she went.

Adolphus sat down in his old place. He knew that he would not eat a good dinner that night. Tomorrow he would have another supply of balloons, and with any luck the weather would be fine and still and there would be plenty of tourists in the square. He did not for one moment believe that Maria would come back to pay for the balloon. How surprised he was, then, when some time later he saw her running towards him across the square carrying one of his balloons. "I caught one," she said, smiling, "and here is the money for it."

"What an honest child you are!" exclaimed Adolphus. "Now at least I can buy a cup of coffee." He patted Maria on the head and went into the café. When he ordered his coffee, the café proprietor said, "So you did sell a balloon after all?"

Adolphus explained about Maria, and when he had drunk his coffee he went back to his seat in the square. There was nothing else he could do until tomorrow, when the train from the city would bring more balloons to sell. He settled himself down to watch the tourists coming and going. Not greatly to his surprise, he soon discovered that they had found his balloons. "I wonder if they know whose balloons they are," thought Adolphus to himself, but he did not speak of it to anyone.

One by one, the tourists went into the café for their morning coffee. "Free balloons in your town," they laughed. "Balloons everywhere." It did not occur to them to wonder whose balloons they were, but the café proprietor took them to the window and pointed towards Adolphus.

"There is the man who owns those balloons," he said, and explained what had happened.

"That's just too bad," scoffed one of the tourists. "He should have taken better care of his balloons."

"Findings keepings," said another.

The café proprietor, who had already made arrangements for Adolphus to have a free meal in his café later that day, was shocked. He looked at Maria, who was sitting by herself in a corner. She was a very small child, and rather shy, but suddenly she seemed to find courage from somewhere. She jumped to her feet. "I paid for mine," she said, "and so should you."

For a moment or two there was silence in the café. The tourists looked down at their hands, at the table, at their feet, anywhere but at Maria, who had made them feel ashamed. Then one man reached into his pocket and took out some money, which he handed to Maria. The others followed suit. Soon every one of the balloons had been paid for, and Maria ran out into the square and handed the money to Adolphus. "Here is the money for your balloons," she said, but she did not tell Adolphus how she had come by it.

Adolphus turned away to hide his tears of gratitude. "Tomorrow," he said, "you must come and see me again, and you shall have the prettiest balloon you ever saw, quite free."

But when he turned around Maria had gone, and he never saw her again.

*   *   *

Follow-up Discussion
Discussion of the statement "finders keepers" should be the natural follow-up to this story. This is a saying which has slight regional variations, but one that is in constant use in school playgrounds all over the country. It is also a statement that is morally incorrect. This story provides an ideal opportunity for teachers to instruct children in the correct procedure to be adopted on finding lost property.

There are many other directions that the discussions can take, as natural progressions or by careful steering by the teacher. For example, there may be talk about honesty and dishonesty, "pangs of conscience", and "feelings of guilt" and the idea that the measure of life's fulfilment is not the amount of money one earns.

Language Development and Creative Writing
Discussion and writing about Adolphus's flight and what the children would expect him to have seen during his excursion with the balloons can give rise to some rich descriptive language.

The children could also be encouraged to talk and write about their feelings when they have done something wrong, even if they have not been detected.

Environmental Studies and Science
The story provides a starting-point for a project on wind or flight. For both these topics there is a wealth of very good published back-up material.

The balloons in the story can lead on to discussing balloons filled with air, hot air and hydrogen and experimenting to see what happens in each case. Young children ask why their party balloons go down. By submersing an inflated balloon in water the children can have that question answered for them.

Mathematics
Much of the mathematics that is suggested by the topic of wind has already been dealt with in the follow-up suggestions to "Mr Brown and His Interesting Dog". On the subject of flight, the children could make different types of paper planes, to see who can make the one that takes the longest to reach the ground. This will involve using a stop-watch to time the flights.

Art and Craft
Adolphus selling his balloons in the square would provide the children with an opportunity to use lots of bold and interesting colours. His view of the square as he is being blown higher and higher by the wind is another painting suggested by this story.

Drama and Movement
This story and the message it conveys make it most suitable for dramatic portrayal in assembly.

There are aspects of the story which are marvellous for use in a dance and mime lesson.

Music
By improvising with a variety of instruments, the children could attempt to capture the sounds made by the wind whistling and howling.

Father Christmas and the Ice Goblins

(Dependability, Teamwork)

Father Christmas had been very busy all the year in his glittering cave at North-by-Nowhere. All the toys had been made; all the games had been invented; all the books had been written. The packing department had worked overtime ever since Midsummer's Day to get all the orders packed up, and now the good little gnomes of North-by-Nowhere were carrying the parcels out to the sleigh.

It was early on Christmas Eve, but because this Christmas promised to be busier than usual, Father Christmas had decided to make an early start. The reindeer were harnessed to the sleigh, pawing the snow and snorting down their nostrils in their eagerness to be off. Father Christmas was in his room putting on an extra pair of socks, whilst his boots stood before the fire to warm.

"Now you are quite sure you won't have anything to eat before you go?" said Mrs Christmas anxiously.

"No time for that, my dear," replied Father Christmas. "I must be off as soon as possible. I never had so many gifts to deliver in all the years I've been doing the job. As to eating and drinking, well, most of the children prepare me a little something for refreshment before they go to bed, so I'm sure I shan't go hungry."

He pulled on his boots and fastened his coat. "Where's my cap?" he said. "I can't find my cap."

"Here it is, dear," said Mrs Christmas. "I just popped it into the oven for a minute to get it nice and warm."

"Mm!" said Father Christmas, as he pulled his cap down over his ears, and he wriggled delightedly as the warmth crept in through his ears and right down to his toes. "Now, my dear," he said, "before I go I'll give you your Christmas present, because it may be very late on Christmas morning by the time I get back."

He pulled out from behind his chair a huge parcel.

Mrs Christmas clapped her hands. "What is it?" she cried.

"Why don't you open it and find out?" chuckled Father Christmas.

"Will that be in order, dear?" she enquired anxiously. "It's not quite Christmas yet, you know."

"To tell you the truth," said Father Christmas, his eyes twinkling merrily, "I have a special reason for wanting you to open it now."

"In that case," said Mrs Christmas, "I will."

She was so excited that she could hardly undo the string, but with a little help from Father Christmas she managed it and opened the box inside.

Her eyes opened wide in astonishment. "Why, it's a complete Father Christmas outfit!" she gasped. "Complete with cap and scarf and boots and – and even a false white beard!"

"That's to keep your chin warm," said Father Christmas. "I couldn't wait for you to grow one."

Mrs Christmas stared at him. "Do you mean – do you really mean that this time I can go with you on your rounds?" she said.

"That's it exactly," chuckled Father Christmas. "I've been giving it quite a lot of thought since last Christmas, and I've decided that you shall. Times have changed, you know, and no-one will be at all surprised to see a lady Father Christmas delivering their presents. Besides," he added, "I'm sure you will do a much better job than some of our gnomes have been doing during the last few years. Such confusion! Parcels left at the wrong houses, some not delivered at all, some dropped in the snow and lost, children's names all mixed up so that they were left gifts that they didn't know what to do with. Oh, such mistakes! The truth is, my dear, that some of those gnomes of ours are too excited to do the job properly. They're far too anxious to be getting back here for their Christmas party. They have their minds on Christmas pudding instead of their deliveries, as I have told them more than once. This time I have told them that they may stay at home and hang up the Christmas decorations in the cave instead."

Mrs Christmas had lost no time and was already dressed in her new Christmas outfit. She gave a twirl. "What do you think?" she enquired archly.

"Very fetching," said Father Christmas. "I'm not too sure about the beard, though. Perhaps it would be as well if you wrapped your scarf around your chin instead. Some children might be frightened at the sight of a lady with a long white beard."

"I'll do that," said Mrs Christmas.

Now, whilst all this had been going on, the Ice Goblins from the Icy Mountain had been creeping nearer and nearer to the cave of North-by-Nowhere, and it was quite obvious by the expression on their faces that they were up to no good. They smiled horrible smiles and they laughed horrible laughs, and their little pointed ears, like daggers, glinted in the moonlight. Nearer and nearer to the sleigh they crept, without anyone noticing their progress across the frozen wastes of snow, for they were white all over, white with the whiteness of ice and snow, and their hearts were as heavy and cold as icebergs in a leaden sea.

They stopped when they came near to the sleigh, and watched the good little gnomes loading the parcels into it. They knew quite well that Father Christmas had delayed his start for a few moments in order to tell Mrs Christmas that she was going with him, and in those few moments they intended to do a shocking thing.

They intended to steal the sleigh!

"Why should the children get presents every Christmas," they said, "when we don't get presents at all?" – for it never occurred to any one of them to make presents for their friends. They were far too wicked for *that*.

At last, the sleigh was ready. All but one of the good little gnomes had run back into the cave to start unpacking the Christmas decorations and to get ready for their Christmas party. The one who was left was the gnome who was fond of animals, and he had stayed behind to give the reindeer some titbits from his hand.

"Why doesn't he go?" hissed the Ice Goblins to each other. (The Ice Goblins always hissed when they were angry, making a sound like the north wind whistling through a keyhole.)

"Let us all hiss together," they said, "so that he shivers and thinks that a snow storm is coming. That should send him back to his cave in a tremble."

So the Ice Goblins all hissed together, and the gnome who was fond of animals looked up at the sky and shivered, and patted the poor reindeer on their necks, and said, "I'll go and fetch some rugs to fasten over your backs to keep you warm on a night like this." And he ran into the cave to get them.

"Ah!" hissed the Ice Goblins, "Ah, there he goes-s-s—s!" Then they rushed out from their hiding place and clambered on to the sleigh. One of them had brought a whip, which he cracked over the back of the leading reindeer, making the poor creature leap into the air in a panic. As you know, Father Christmas *never* uses a whip on his reindeer, so the animal couldn't understand what he had done to deserve such treatment. He galloped away into the sky to try to get away from the thing that was hurting his back, but the faster he went, the harder the Ice Goblin lashed him. With the reins in their hands, the Ice Goblins guided the reindeer towards the Icy Mountain, making a grotesque silhouette across the face of the moon.

When the gnome who was fond of animals came out of the cave with the rugs, he was just in time to see who had stolen the sleigh. He cried out, "Father Christmas! Father Christmas, come quickly and see! The Ice Goblins have stolen the sleigh!" But by the time Father Christmas and Mrs Christmas and the good little gnomes had come out of the cave, the sleigh had disappeared. They looked to the north and they looked to the south; they looked to the east and the west, but no trace of the sleigh could they see. And the good little gnomes fell down on their knees and wept.

All over the world the children were preparing for bed, not knowing that the sleigh had been stolen. "Now don't you forget," the grown-ups were saying. "If you don't go to sleep, Father Christmas won't come!" The children hung up their stockings and put out food and drink for the good man when he came. Then they shut their eyes tightly and did their very best to go to sleep. But it's never easy to fall asleep on Christmas Eve, and they couldn't do it, however hard they tried.

And then a strange thing happened. Upon each child's bed there appeared a good little gnome. The children were not afraid. They knew they were Christmas gnomes because of the little red caps they wore, so they sat up in bed and asked them what they wanted.

"The Ice Goblins have stolen the sleigh," said the gnomes, "and all the presents are gone. Will you help us to get them back?"

When the children agreed, the gnomes took them by the hand and danced them away to the caverns of North-by-Nowhere, where they met Father Christmas, and *he* led them across the snow to the Icy Mountain where the Ice Goblins lived.

"Join hands," Father Christmas instructed them, "and make a circle around the Icy Mountain, and when the circle is complete you will see what happens."

The children did as he said, and when the last two children

had joined their hands together and the circle was complete they heard a strange noise.

Drip, drip, drip, it went; and splash, splash, splash, it went. The Ice Goblins were melting away with the warmth that was coming from the children's hearts. And before long, all that was left of the Ice Goblins was a lake that formed into ice as it froze.

Father Christmas went into the Icy Mountain and drove his sleigh out, and the gnome who was fond of animals gave the reindeer a bit of something special to compensate for their terrible ordeal. Then the children cheered as they skated back home to bed.

Late, very late that night, Father Christmas and Mrs Christmas made their calls upon the children. Some of the gifts got a bit mixed up and went to the wrong houses, but that was quite understandable under the circumstances, what with the last-minute rush and Mrs Christmas being new to the job, but she has improved since then and there's no doubt that, in time, she will get it absolutely right. When that happens, I suppose, not a single child in the world will be overlooked at Christmas, and that will be something to sing about, won't it?

*   *   *

Follow-up Discussion
This story contains many points which can be enlarged upon if it is used as an assembly theme. The title suggests that this is a Christmas story, but the moral implications are much more far-reaching.

By its very nature, Christmas-time tends to bring out in people caring and thoughtful attitudes towards others. Unfortunately, these attitudes do not always extend beyond the festive season, which makes all the goodwill rather meaningless.

The press and the media bring home atrocities which happen all too frequently, locally, nationally and internationally, the realities of life. If children can be encouraged to realize that the world in which they are growing up will only change if they themselves grow up with the determination to improve it, there could be hope for the future. Their aim must be that when they are adults they will work together towards building a society in which consideration and caring for others will replace those values which are at the root of present-day social problems.

Language Development and Creative Writing
The story is rich in stimuli for lively and colourful description of the cold north wind and tingling ears, noses and fingers. The children could think of onomatopoeic words to describe the Icy Mountain melting.

Environmental Studies

A research project into Christmas in other countries could be a profitable follow-up to this story. The children could be encouraged to write to children in other countries as part of the project.

The story of St Nicholas and his good deeds could be told in conjunction with the project and the children could research into the origin of the names Father Christmas and Santa Claus.

Christmas has become a time when pets are given as presents and later neglected or even abandoned. The gnome who looked after the reindeer provides a perfect opening for talking about caring for family pets.

Art and Craft

There are many points in the story which can be painted. The children could make reindeers and a sleigh.

Drama

"Father Christmas and the Ice Goblins" is ideal for use as a play for assembly, and can be adapted for use as a class production for a Christmas concert, using music and dance. The children can compose their own percussion music for the "north wind whistling through a key-hole", icicles forming and the Icy Mountain melting. Audience participation can be encouraged to help to overcome the Ice Goblins.

Sam Snuffett

(Caring and Sharing)

There once lived a selfish man named Sam Snuffett. Sam hated to share anything with anybody. He wouldn't share his apartment; he wouldn't share his food; and if anybody said, "Can you tell me what time it is, please?", he wouldn't even share the time of day with them.

Naturally, Sam Snuffett was very miserable. He *knew* he was miserable, but couldn't think why. He used to go into the park every day to watch the ducks. He thought the park and the ducks belonged to him, which just goes to show that he was not only selfish, but rather foolish, too.

One day, when Sam was sitting on his usual park bench (which nobody else ever dared to share with him, because he glared at them so), there came a sudden shower of rain.

"You'll get wet if you stay out there in the rain," called the Park Keeper. "Come into the shelter with me."

Sam looked very sly. "Oh no," he said. "I'm not falling for that one. If I come over there, somebody will come along and take my bench, and I won't have that." So he stayed where he was, and got very wet. When the shower had passed, the sun came out and a beautiful rainbow appeared over the duck pond.

As Sam sat there admiring it, two children came skipping along. "Look at the rainbow!" cried one of them, pointing.

"It seems to come down right in the middle of the pond!" laughed the other, and they both stood there looking in wonder at the rainbow.

Sam became very angry because the children were sharing the rainbow with him. He wanted it all to himself. He was just about to tell them to go away when a lady and gentleman came along, arm in arm. "Oh, what a beautiful rainbow!" cried the lady. "Let us sit down on this bench and look at it."

The lady and gentleman, who were strangers to that part of

town and who didn't know Sam Snuffett, sat down on the bench alongside him and gazed at the beautiful sight.

Sam was furious. Four people sharing his rainbow now – and as if that wasn't enough, the Park Keeper was standing in his shelter looking at the rainbow as if he had never seen one before. How dare they look at his rainbow, thought Sam? He had seen it first, so it belonged to him. He decided to do something about it.

Without thinking very hard about what he was doing, Sam jumped up and rushed over to the pond. He was already wet, so he leapt into the water and waded out to the middle of the pond where the rainbow came down.

"What are you doing in the pond?" cried the astonished Park Keeper. "You're frightening the ducks!" And there was no doubt that the ducks were frightened. They must have thought that Sam Snuffett was a very peculiar duck indeed, for they scuttled about the surface of the water crying out to each other that they had never seen anything like it in all their born days.

Sam grasped hold of the end of the rainbow (or so he thought) and rolled it up in a bundle. Then he waded out of the pond and ran back home as fast as his legs would carry him. But when he got back to his apartment and placed his precious bundle on the table, he saw that it was only an armful of pond weed and an old banana skin which somebody had thrown into the pond. He was very cross, and jumped up and down shaking his fists, and he couldn't sleep that night for thinking that he had left the rainbow in the park for the other people to admire.

A few days later Sam was walking along the street where he lived, when the sun came peeping through a little hole in the clouds and a ray of sunlight came right down into the street. It was so lovely, so bright and shiny and new, that Sam decided that it should be his. Running quickly along the street, he saw that it came down right inside an open dustbin into which an old lady had just been depositing some rubbish.

Quick as a flash, Sam jumped over her fence, and snatching the lid of the dustbin from the terrified old lady, he slammed it on, trapping the sunbeam inside (or so he thought). He then picked up the dustbin and staggered back home with it – all the way along the street, into his apartment block, and up the stairs, and in through his own door. He could hardly wait to open it up and look inside, but when he did, all that he found was a heap of tin cans, smelly cabbage, and soggy cardboard boxes. He could have wept with anger, but he didn't have time for that, because by then the old lady had been to fetch a policeman to get her dustbin back.

Sam was taken off to the police station. "Stealing a dustbin?" said the sergeant. "Why did you want to steal a dustbin, of all things?"

"My sunbeam was inside," said Sam sullenly.

"Oh no it wasn't," snapped the old lady.

The sergeant, who knew all about Sam Snuffett, said, "We'd better settle this once and for all. Take everything out of the dustbin and make quite sure that your sunbeam isn't there."

Sam started to protest, but the sergeant was having none of that. He stood by, whilst Sam took out every tin can, and every smelly cabbage leaf, and each little bit of soggy cardboard. It was not a pleasant task, but the sergeant made him finish it. "Well?" he said. "Is your sunbeam there?"

"No," said Sam.

"Then go home," said the sergeant, "and try not to be so selfish again."

After that, Sam was careful about what he did, but he hadn't learned his lesson yet. One day, in the wintertime, he awoke to find that it was snowing. How beautiful it looked, so fresh and crisp and new! The children, with their dogs, were down there in the street, making snowballs, and the old lady whose dustbin he had stolen was down there, too, helping a little girl to make a snowman.

Sam threw open his window. "Go away!" he shouted. "Leave my snow alone!"

The children looked up. One of them, wiser than the rest, shouted back, "Come on down, Sam, and join us!"

But Sam was holding out a saucepan to try to catch some of the snow as it fell, so that the children should not have it all. He stood there a long time, until he was cold and stiff. Then he pulled in the saucepan and took it into the kitchen.

All that was inside was a tiny pool of water, but outside in the street the children and the old lady were still having fun. He went back to his window and watched them.

"Come down, Sam!" cried the wise child again. "There's plenty of snow for everybody."

Sam went down. The children didn't say, "You have been a selfish man, Sam, so you shall not share in the fun." Instead, they allowed him to join in their games. Sam was amazed. He was having fun! He had never had fun before. He began to smile. Suddenly he didn't feel miserable any more.

And do you know what? The next time there was a rainbow over the pond, Sam Snuffett didn't try to capture it for himself. He ran off to fetch the children to share it with him, because, as he had discovered, sharing is fun.

*   *   *

Follow-up Discussion
The message in this story is very clear. Sam Snuffett's selfishness leads him into embarrassing situations and eventually into the arms of the law.

It is not the warning he receives from the policeman that really makes him mend his ways, but the generous invitation from a child to come and share their fun in the snow. Sam accepts and finds to his amazement that he is no longer miserable.

This discovery leads Sam to the conclusion that much more enjoyment is to be gained by sharing rather than trying to grasp things for himself.

Language Development and Creative Writing
The descriptive passages give the opportunity for the children to discuss and write about rainbows, sunbeams and snowstorms.

Environmental Studies
The follow-up work suggested by this story, such as work on rainbows, weather, parks and recreation grounds, has been dealt with in connection with other stories. (See pages 125, 133, 138.)

Mathematics and Science
When there is snow, some very valuable work in weighing and capacity can be done with it. Find out if there is any loss in weight or capacity of amounts of snow and the water that it produces on melting.

Art and Craft
There are several descriptive passages in the story which can be used as stimuli for art work. The rainbow and the pond in the park and the sunbeam shining through the hole in the cloud are just two examples.

Drama
This is a wonderful story for dramatization in assembly. It affords a good opportunity for a child with a sense of comedy to play Sam.

The Princess and the Rainbow

(Concern for the Environment, Teamwork)

Once upon a magic time there lived a princess whose name was Rain Blossom. Princess Rain Blossom was very beautiful, so beautiful that her hand was sought in marriage by every king and every prince that ever set eyes upon her.

But Princess Rain Blossom refused them all. Although she was a princess she cared very little for fine living. Her greatest pleasures were in the world of nature; she loved the woods and the rivers, wild flowers, birds, and butterflies; but most of all she loved the rainbow.

After rain had fallen she would run out into the meadows and watch the rainbow appear overhead. It seemed to her the most beautiful sight in the whole wide world, and she would stand as if transfixed by its beauty until it faded and disappeared.

One day, whilst she was standing thus, there appeared before her a handsome young prince. He told Rain Blossom that he was the prince of the rainbow, and that he had seven sisters whose occupation it was to carry the ribbons of the rainbow across the sky, each one carrying ribbons of a different colour. Only by sliding down the rainbow, he said, could he come to earth. "We have often watched you," he said, "standing in the meadows gazing up at the rainbow, and today we decided to come and speak to you. Here are my sisters." He held up his hand and one by one the rainbow princesses came dancing out of the sky; the princess of the red ribbons, the princess of the orange ribbons, and so on, until last of all, a little out of breath and rather out of step, came Violet. She was the smallest one of all, but she was especially beloved of her brother and her sisters.

They were delighted with their new friend Rain Blossom. They showed her how they danced their ribbons into a rainbow. They gently teased their sister Violet because she never could arrive on time. And, of course, the prince of the rainbow fell in love with

Rain Blossom, and she with him. All too soon it was time for the princesses to wrap up their rainbow and put it away until next time, so they had to part.

Princess Rain Blossom waited eagerly for the next shower of rain that would bring the prince and his sisters back to earth. One day there came a terrible storm, presided over by the king of the storm himself. In her eagerness to meet the prince again Rain Blossom ran out into the meadows before the storm had quite abated, and the king of the storm saw her for the very first time. He was immediately struck with her beauty, and determined to make her his queen. He descended to earth in his great grey chariot and told the trembling princess that he had come to claim her for his bride. She shrank from him and told him that she could never marry him, for she loved the prince of the rainbow.

When he heard this the king of the storm was very angry. His eyes flashed lightning and in a voice of thunder he commanded his servants, the storm imps, to capture the princess and carry her off to his castle in the sky, behind the big black cloud that lingers in the east. There she should remain, he said, until she came to her senses and agreed to become his queen.

When the storm had passed by, the rainbow princesses wove their rainbow and the prince descended to the earth. He was distressed to find that Rain Blossom was not there to welcome him. He called her to the north and to the south, to the east and the west, but she was far away in the sky and could not hear him. He called his sisters to help him in the search. Violet, as before, was the last to arrive, a little out of breath and rather out of step, but she told her brother that, being late, she had seen princess Rain Blossom being carried away by the storm imps.

"That can mean only one thing," he groaned. "She has been taken to the castle of the king of the storm, behind the big black cloud that lingers in the east. We can never reach her there." And in his grief he flung himself down on the ground, and wept.

His sisters were overcome with pity. They communed with each other as to how they could help him. Soon they had a plan. "We must build a rainbow," they said, "that reaches all the way to the castle of the king of the storm, even though we must take it beyond the big black cloud that lingers in the east. We must take it right to the room where Rain Blossom lies. That is the only way."

The prince was alarmed at the danger to which his sisters were willing to expose themselves, but they told him that unless they were reunited with their dear Rain Blossom, whom they had hoped would become their sister, they would never again have the heart to dance a rainbow. It was Violet's tears and his love for Rain Blossom that made the prince agree to the plan.

The seven sisters began to dance, blending their ribbons together as they went – red into orange, orange into yellow, yellow into green, and blue, and indigo, and last of all, a little out of breath and rather out of step, came Violet. Up and up they went, curving over towards the east, towards the big black cloud beyond which they could not see, fearless in their great love for their brother and his beloved princess. As they approached the castle of the king of the storm, the storm imps came out to accost them, plucking with their sharp little fingers at the rainbow ribbons, blowing their icy breath on to the faces of the rain princesses, so that even red and orange turned a little blue. But bravely they went on with their dance.

The king of the storm himself came out to try to turn them back, but they were too skilful for him. They danced around him, binding him up with their ribbons until he could not move, so that even to this day he can still be heard complaining behind the big black cloud that lingers in the east.

At last, the rainbow princesses danced their way into the room where the imprisoned Rain Blossom lay. She was overjoyed to see them. They took her to the window and she beheld her prince ascending the rainbow towards her. Taking her in his arms he lifted her on to the rainbow, and together they slid to the earth.

They were married in the springtime, in the meadows, though the ceremony *was* somewhat delayed on account of the smallest bridesmaid arriving late, a little out of breath and rather out of step. And we all know by now who *that* was.

*   *   *

Follow-up Discussion
There are two moral themes which thread their way through this story; enjoyment and appreciation of the environment and teamwork in overcoming adversity. The second point is probably the more poignant.

The children can be encouraged to look at the natural groups in which they themselves are involved in their normal everyday life. They are members of three; the family, their class and the school as a whole.

By referring to the way the princesses use their combined efforts to overcome the King of the Storm, the children can be helped into the realization that harmony in the home, classroom and school requires a certain amount of effort on everybody's part.

Most children will have experienced examples of disharmony. Some may be encouraged to talk about their feelings when these situations arise. The older children might even appreciate that, on occasions, they might have been the cause of the disharmony.

The children who are in any way involved with team activities, even the potted sports we often use in games lessons, will be familiar with teamwork. In these incidents they will have witnessed the uncoordinated child who lets the team down. This story, in particular Violet, might help the children to appreciate that encouragement, not criticism, is the best way to help to draw that child back into the framework of the team.

Language Development and Creative Writing
The rainbow colours can be remembered by the mnemonic "Richard of York gave battle in Vain". The children could make up their own personal mnemonics from the initial letters of the colours of the rainbow.

Environmental Studies and Science
After reading this story the subject of colours and rainbows could be explored. Colour-mixing with both paints and lights and the use of prisms to project a spectrum onto a sheet of card are just some of the possible extensions.

Art and Craft
Painting rainbows and further work on mixing paints to achieve different shades could prove satisfying.

Drama and Dance
This story has a lot of potential for use as a production, involving dance with coloured ribbons.

Barney and the Easter Chicken

(Caring and Sharing, Honesty)

On Easter Day Barney had a beautiful, big Easter egg from his Mum and Dad. It had sugar flowers on the front, with Happy Easter written in white icing, and it was packed up in a box with a purple ribbon round it. When he had looked at it he ran to the window to wait for Gran. He always had an extra-special Easter egg from Gran. Last year it had been a special one with his own name written on it, and the year before that it had been a surprise egg, with two little eggs inside it. He couldn't remember farther back than that, but he knew that Gran always went to a lot of trouble to find something different for him.

At last he saw her coming up the garden path, and she was carrying something very carefully in her hands. Barney ran to open the door.

"Hello, Barney," she said. "Happy Easter."

"Happy Easter, Gran," said Barney, looking at the box in her hands.

Gran laughed. "Yes, this is for you," she said. "You must open it very carefully."

Barney took the box to the table and took off the wrappings. It wasn't an egg at all, but a chocolate chicken!

"Oh, Gran," said Mum, "you have been to a lot of trouble again!"

"Not at all," Gran replied. "I knew that Barney would have an egg from you, and I saw this in the shop and it took my eye. I don't know why, but there seems to be something rather magical about it."

Barney leaned his chin on his arms and looked at the chicken. He felt that Gran was quite right; there was something magical about it. The chicken had an eye on each side of its head, and although the left eye was quite an ordinary round chocolate eye, the right one had a kind of sparkle in it, and it seemed to be staring right back at Barney, as if it knew what he was thinking.

He carried the chicken to the sideboard and left it there all morning, but each time he happened to look at it the chicken seemed to be staring back with that sparkling eye. It was very strange. The chicken watched him eat his lunch. It watched him as he left the table. It watched him as he went out into the garden to play. He took his Easter egg out with him.

Now the sad thing about Barney was that sometimes he found it hard to tell the truth. Mum and Dad had sometimes found him out for lying, and they had been quite worried about it, but Gran said that it was something he would grow out of. "Just leave him alone," he had heard her say to Mum when they didn't know he was listening. "Something will happen to make him realize that it's better to tell the truth."

When Barney got out into the garden he saw his friend Helen playing in the garden next door with her twin sisters and her baby brother. The children next door didn't get as many treats as Barney did because they hadn't got a father. Barney wondered if they had had an Easter egg.

He sat down in a place where they couldn't see him and started to eat his egg. He thought he would eat half of it and share the rest with Helen and her sisters and brother, but when he had eaten the first half he felt that he could eat just a little bit more, and before he knew what had happened, it was all gone.

When he went back indoors with the empty box Gran exclaimed, "Your Easter egg gone already! Surely you didn't eat all that yourself?"

"No," said Barney, "I shared it with Helen and the others next door."

"That was kind of you," said Gran, and Mum looked pleased.

Suddenly Barney felt rather sick. He also felt that he was being watched. Somehow his eyes were drawn to the chocolate chicken on the sideboard, and he met the gaze of that strange, sparkling eye that seemed to stare right into his head. He wished he hadn't said that about sharing the egg with Helen.

Just before Gran went home Dad said, "Aren't you going to offer Gran a piece of the chocolate chicken she brought you?"

Barney looked at the chicken again. He wondered if it knew that he had quite a bad pain in his tum.

"That's all right," Gran said. "I don't really fancy any

chocolate just now. You'd better save it for another day, Barney. You've had quite enough for one day."

Mum laughed. "He can't have had much," she said, "if he shared it with four other children."

"Perhaps not," said Gran, as she buttoned up her coat. She kissed Barney goodbye, which made him feel worse than ever. He was glad when it was time for bed and he didn't have to look at the chicken any more.

In the morning he went downstairs. He didn't feel sick, but he still felt uncomfortable when he looked at the chicken. Later in the morning he decided to take it out into the garden. The children next door were just coming round to play with him. Helen was pushing Jamie in his pushchair, and when he saw the chocolate chicken his eyes grew round and he made funny little noises and reached out to grab it.

"Did you have that for Easter?" Helen asked.

"Yes," said Barney, "from my Gran."

"We haven't got a Gran," said one of the twins wistfully.

"But we had an egg from our Mom," said Helen. "We shared it."

Barney looked down at the chicken. One egg between four wasn't much. "Would you like to share my chicken?" he asked.

"Yes please!" shouted the twins, and Helen smiled as little Jamie kicked his legs in delight.

Helen broke the chicken into pieces. Barney didn't dare to. They all sat down on the grass and nibbled the chocolate. It tasted quite ordinary. "Have you got the head?" Barney asked Helen.

"Yes," she said.

"It's got one funny sparkly eye," said Barney thoughtfully.

She looked at it closely. "It's only made of sugar," she said, and popped it in her mouth. Barney heard her crunching it, and was very glad to see her swallow it down. Suddenly he felt very much better than he had done since yesterday morning.

When he ran indoors he said to Mum, "Guess what? The chicken had one eye that was made of sugar. Helen ate it."

"Oh?" said Mum, kneeling down and giving him one of her special hugs. "Did you share Gran's chicken with the children next door?"

"Yes," said Barney, and this time he felt much more comfortable about saying it. Maybe it was because the chicken had gone. Maybe it was because he knew that Mum believed him. Maybe it was because Gran had been right and there had been something magical about the chocolate chicken. Gran was usually right.

*   *   *

Follow-up Discussion
"Honesty is the best policy" is clearly the message in this story. The sparkling right eye of the chicken makes Barney feel pangs of guilt about having told a lie about sharing his Easter egg.

The last paragraph poses several questions about why Barney felt much more comfortable. The children could consider why Barney felt this way.

Helen, her twin sisters and her baby brother were not as fortunate as Barney. They did not have a father or a generous gran to lavish presents on them. This could lead into a discussion about people who are less fortunate than ourselves and what can be done to help them.

Language Development and Creative Writing
A chicken is just one example of a new life just beginning. Around Easter-time there are many other examples. The story could be used as an Easter story to stimulate work on Spring, New Life and Growth.

Environmental Studies and Science
Easter is by tradition the time for chickens. It might be possible for the children to incubate some eggs, or, if this is not possible, the children could visit a poultry farm.

Art and Craft
There are many art and craft activities which the subjects Easter, Spring or chickens will stimulate. Easter chickens can be made with handprints, the fingers looking like feathers.

Drama
The story can be adapted for use as a play, but would probably be of more value as a reading.

The Silver Dollar

(Honesty)

It was a bright and sunny morning, so bright that Narain sneezed when he looked up at the sky. All over the park the sun was shining on leaves, and water, and stones. Narain walked slowly behind his father, who was talking to a friend as they strolled around the park. There was something in the air that felt like magic; Narain believed in magic, even though his father said it was all nonsense.

How shiny the pebbles were! Here and there in the grass they gleamed like jewels, and several times Narain stopped to pick one up and gaze at it in wonder. Suddenly, he saw something shining brighter than any of the pebbles. Perhaps it was a piece of broken glass, he thought. He ran towards it. His father had always taught him to remove pieces of broken glass that were lying about, because they were dangerous. He stooped down to pick up the glass in the way he had been taught to do it, when, to his surprise, he found that he was looking at a bright and shiny silver dollar.

He picked it up. His father and his friend were sitting down on a seat, talking quietly together. Narain knew that the coin didn't belong to either of them, for they hadn't walked anywhere near the place where he had found it, but there were many other people about who might have dropped it. He stood for a moment, wondering which person he should enquire of first. He wished he didn't feel so strange, so curiously light, as he walked towards a man who was walking along the path, but then, he always felt like that when he started thinking about magic. "Excuse me," he said. "Have you lost a silver dollar?"

The man smiled, but it wasn't a very pleasant smile. "A silver dollar?" he repeated, looking down at the coin which Narain was holding in his hand. "Yes," he went on, "it is mine. It's a good luck charm." He stretched out his hand to take the silver dollar from Narain, but suddenly he stopped as if he had been turned to stone. Narain stared at the man and reluctantly placed the coin in the man's outstretched palm, but the man still didn't move. He remained as still as a statue. Narain touched him and gave him a gentle push, but still he did not move. "Aha," thought Narain. "I know all about you. It *is* a magic day and the silver dollar doesn't belong to you, so you have been enchanted." He quickly retrieved the silver dollar from the man's palm and ran off, leaving the man standing there in the same attitude, still as stone.

A little way off were two boys playing football. Narain went up to them. "Have you lost a silver dollar?" he asked very politely.

The boys grinned at each other. "Oh yes," said one. "Give it to me."

"No," said the other boy. "It's mine."

Narain smiled at them, for no sooner had they spoken than they, too, had been turned into statues.

His father and his friend were still talking, and neither of them seemed to have noticed that anything was amiss. Narain looked around once more. There was a lady pushing a baby carriage, in which a little boy was sitting, screaming because he couldn't have an ice cream. Narain had noticed the same lady walking by the place a little earlier, so he went up to her and put the question to her.

The lady looked at the baby and then at the coin in Narain's hand. She hesitated for a few moments, but then she said, "Why, yes, of course I have! I wondered where I had lost it. Let me have it, please."

As she stretched out her hand, she became rigid. Even the baby stopped screaming, and sat there with his mouth wide open. Narain was sorry for the baby, but there was nothing he could do for him, so he went to some other people who were having a picnic on the grass. They all laughed when Narain asked his question, and one of them said that Narain would learn to be less foolish as he grew older, but all of them claimed the silver dollar as their own. Soon they were all sitting quite still, unable to move.

At last, an old lady came along. She was looking down at the ground as if she was searching for something, and there was an anxious look on her face. Narain approached her. "Are you looking for this?" he asked, holding out the silver dollar.

The old lady gasped and threw up her hands in delight. "My silver dollar!" she cried. "It was given to me many years ago by a very dear friend, and I would rather lose everything else I possess in the world, than that. What a good, kind child you are to return it to me." Her hand closed around the coin as Narain placed it on her palm. She did not turn into a statue, but hurried away with many expressions of gratitude.

Narain hurried back to his father, who was just shaking hands with his friend. "Well, Narain," he said. "Did you have fun with all your friends?"

"Oh, yes," said Narain, looking back at all the people, who were just beginning to come out of their trances, and who didn't seem to know what had happened to them. "Did you enjoy talking to your friend?"

"Very much indeed," replied his father. "We had a nice long talk about the way people are behaving these days, but I am afraid that we came to the conclusion that there is a great deal of dishonesty about. There are many people who don't seem to know what honesty is."

Narain smiled as he fell into step beside them. "I do," he said.

*   *   *

Follow-up Discussion
There can be very few people who have never done anything dishonest. Ask the children to consider the question of their own honesty. As they remember the last time they told a lie, the children are told to assume a statue position. A teacher can be appointed to judge the funniest statue.

After this variation of the statue game the children can be encouraged to discuss how uncomfortable and embarrassing it would be if this happened every time we told a lie.

Adults are guilty of sowing the seeds of many similar misconceptions about dishonesty in the minds of young children, such as "spots appearing on the tongue". These are examples of attempts to discourage dishonesty in children. Talk to the children about how society deals with serious cases.

Another line of discussion that can be pursued is to consider Narain's strategy in trying to locate the owner of the silver coin. Was Narain's question a sensible one? Can the children give any suggestions for a more sensible way to ask the question?

Language Development and Creative Writing
From time to time everybody mislays an item of sentimental value and the children can be stimulated into talking and writing about their feelings when they have lost or broken their favourite toy.

Environmental Studies

The word "dollar" opens up the opportunity to do some follow-up work on currencies.

The children could also look at parks and recreation grounds as local amenities.

Mathematics

As an extension of the work on currencies, the children can look at how other countries break down their metric money into smaller units.

Art and Craft

The walk in the park can act as a starting point for planning a park, recreation ground or adventure playground, culminating in making a model of it.

Drama and Movement

This is an excellent story for use as a play in assembly.

In a music and drama lesson the children could devise different ways of playing statues.

Farmer John and the Night of the Terrible Storm

(Consideration for Others)

It was a dark and stormy night. The wind howled and roared out of a sky that was as black as pitch. The rain came down in sheets. Farmer John sat dozing before the fire, feeling warm and comfortable, and glad that he was indoors on a night like that.

He was just thinking that he would take his candle and go upstairs to bed when he heard a tap-tap-tapping at the door. "Who can that be?" he asked himself. "People ought to stay by their own firesides on stormy nights instead of bothering good folks like me." But as the tapping continued he got up and opened the door.

"What is it?" he shouted into the darkness. "What do you want?"

At first he could see no-one, but then, happening to glance down, he was astonished to see all his chickens huddled on the doorstep. They were wet and bedraggled and were huddled close together for warmth. "Farmer John," pleaded one of them, "won't you let us come in? There's a hole in the roof of our hut and the rain is pouring in. We are wet and cold and thoroughly miserable. We can't lay eggs for you when we are in such a sorry state as this."

Farmer John thought for a moment. "That's true," he murmured quietly to himself. "Everyone knows that happy chickens lay better eggs than those that are otherwise. I must have my eggs for breakfast and my eggs to take to market. I'd better let them in." He stood back and said in a louder voice, "Come in, all of you, and find a roost on the kitchen dresser."

The chickens came in and settled themselves comfortably. They began to cluck happily among themselves, for Farmer John's kitchen was warm and quiet. Farmer John returned to his seat in the ingle-nook to warm his feet before he went to bed.

Suddenly there was a gentle knock on the door, a little louder than the chickens' tap-tap-tap, but not so loud for all that. Farmer John got up again and opened the door. There stood his little flock of sheep, all shivering so much that they could hardly stand. "What brings you to my door on such a night?" demanded Farmer John. "I left you in the pen with a good strong covering of wattles. Surely you can't complain about that?"

"But the wattles were not so strong," protested one of the sheep. "They blew away in the first gust of wind; and the brook burst its banks and flooded us out. There is nowhere for us to shelter from the storm. Please let us come into your kitchen. If we don't dry out our fleeces we shall take cold and die."

"That's quite possible," thought Farmer John, "and if I don't shear them twice a year and sell their wool in the market I shall soon become very poor." So he threw the door open wide and allowed the sheep to come in.

As the sheep settled themselves on the kitchen floor, Farmer John put on his long striped nightshirt and the cap with the tassel on the end, took his candle, and went towards the stairs. "Goodnight, chickens," he said. "Goodnight, sheep."

He had just put his foot on the first stair when there came yet another knock upon the door. Farmer John opened it. There stood Nancy, his goat, her knees knocking together and her eyes wild with fear. "Oh, Farmer John," she quavered, "please let me come in. I am so afraid of the noise and the darkness that I fear I shall never yield another drop of milk!"

"That would be a tragedy!" cried Farmer John. "There's nothing I like better than a cup of goat's milk, and besides, it fetches a very good price in the market. You'd better come in and find yourself a cosy place for the night."

Nancy came in and looked around. "There's very little room in the kitchen," she said, "and I don't get on very well with sheep and chickens, so I will lie down on the landing outside your bedroom door."

Farmer John was not quite sure that he approved of that idea, but he was anxious about Nancy's milk, so he followed her upstairs, stepped over her as she lay down on the mat, and went into his bedroom.

There was a big log fire in Farmer John's bedroom, and a great four-poster bed piled high with warm blankets and eiderdowns. He was a man who liked his comfort, and when he climbed into bed he was very comfortable indeed. So comfortable, in fact, that when a further knock came at the door he was extremely reluctant to get out. However, the knocking became so persistent that there was nothing he could do but wrap a shawl around himself and go downstairs to see who was there.

When he opened the door he was none too pleased to see his old cart-horse Dolly standing there. She looked terrified. The whites of her eyes flashed, and she was trembling from head to foot. "What is it, Dolly?" demanded Farmer John impatiently. "I know I left you securely stabled for the night, with your stall properly closed and plenty of good warm straw for you to lie in, so why have you disturbed me like this?"

"There's a loose board somewhere in my stable that flaps in the wind and keeps me awake," she told him. "The rats have come in to keep dry and have been running over my feet and terrifying me with their squeals and squeaks. Oh, for pity's sake, Farmer John, let me come in with you!"

"This is quite serious," thought Farmer John. "I have to go to market tomorrow to take the eggs and the wool and the goat's milk, and if Dolly is left alone in the stable all night she will be in no fit state to make the journey into town tomorrow." So he held the door open wide, and Dolly came in.

She, too, peeped into the kitchen. "No room in there," she said. "I think I'll go upstairs."

By the light of Farmer John's candle she trotted up the stairs and stepped over Nancy, who was snoring gently on the mat. She went into Farmer John's bedroom and looked around. "What a comfortable-looking bed!" she whinnied. "I think I'll sleep in there tonight." And before Farmer John could think of a way of stopping her, she had jumped into his bed and pulled the eiderdown over her head.

Farmer John got in beside her, feeling quite pleased with himself for his own kindness towards the animals. He was just dropping off to sleep when yet another knock was heard. "If that is the pigs," he told himself angrily, "they must fend for themselves tonight. I'll have none of *them* in my house!"

But it wasn't the pigs. When he opened the door he saw an old man standing on the step. "Who are you?" he shouted. "Knocking on my door in the dead of night and disturbing honest people. Go back to your own home, for I have no more room in here."

"I have no home," returned the old man, "and I have walked far

– very far. I am worn out and soaked to the skin. I am cold. All I ask is a corner in which I can lie down to sleep. Surely you won't refuse me that?"

"What claim have you upon my charity?" demanded Farmer John. "You don't give me eggs, or wool, or milk, and you don't work for me. Why should I shelter you?" And he shut the door in the old man's face and went back to bed.

It was an uncomfortable night with Dolly kicking all her legs in bed, but Farmer John slept a little. He awoke just as dawn was in the sky. He was cold and very stiff. He shook himself, and found to his surprise that he wasn't in his bed at all, but sitting before the fire in the ingle-nook. "Then it was all a dream!" he said, and began to laugh. He blew some life back into the embers of the fire, then he had breakfast and went outside.

There were the chickens pecking their corn in the yard. The goat was in her hut, the horse was in the stable, the sheep were in their pen. "There were no animals in my house last night at all," he chuckled. "What a silly dream it was!" He tried to put the whole thing out of his mind, but one thing would not go away – the recollection of how he had turned away the old man from his door. "But what does it matter?" he asked himself. "It was only a dream."

Nevertheless, as he collected the eggs and milked the goat and sheared the sheep, he felt uneasy in his mind. He went to get Dolly to harness her to his cart. He stopped when he came to her stall, looking down with great distress and terrible guilt, for there on the floor at Dolly's feet was the old man. "He is dead!" he cried. "Oh, why did I turn him away in my dream?"

Suddenly, however, the old man stirred. "Please help me," he begged. "I am weak from hunger and feverish with cold. I came here last night at the height of the storm. I wanted to knock on your door and ask for assistance, but I was afraid that you would refuse to let me in."

Farmer John made no reply. He assisted the old man into the house and seated him beside the kitchen fire. He gave him food and drink. He provided dry clothes and hot water in which to bathe. Then he went and harnessed Dolly to the cart and rode off to market, a wiser and a better man.

*　　　*　　　*

Follow-up Discussion
The discussion that will result from this story will centre around the farmer's attitude in his dream to the old man from whom he did not expect to gain anything in return. The children should consider the question "Should we always expect something in return for doing somebody a favour?"

Language Development and Creative Writing
"Farmer John" is rich in discussion stimuli, particularly for language development. The figurative words and phrases will need to be explained, for example: "The sky was black as pitch"; "the rain came down in sheets". There are also words like "ingle-nook" and "wattle" that will require explanation.

The opening paragraph can be quoted as a fine example of creating the sort of atmosphere that encourages the reader to want to continue with the story. The older children should be encouraged to think of their own stories and to try to employ more imagination in starting their stories than the usual "Once upon a time . . ." or "One day I. . .".

Environmental Studies and Science
The story opens up many different possible follow-up activities, such as studies of Rain, Storms, and Farm Animals. All three topics are well-documented for both teachers and children in this age group.

Mathematics
Mathematics activities in connection with rainfall measurement and recording, temperature readings and other weather details are already part of the normal daily routine in most schools. There are also many attractive and original ways of representing these findings pictorially.

Art and Craft
Rain and storms are evocative subjects for activities in art and craft. A wall frieze with removable figures and features which can be changed according to the weather is just one example of what can be made.

Drama
The story could be adapted for use as a play, but it will require quite a lot of preparation of costumes for the animals.

CHAPTER THREE

Animals

Frogmorton

*(Consideration for Others, Cheerfulness in Adversity,
Caring and Sharing, Concern for the Environment)*

There was once a frog, sitting all alone on a lily leaf, minding his
own business and thinking of nothing in particular, when all of a
sudden a witch came along and turned him into a prince.

He was *furious*. He didn't want to be a prince and live in a palace
and drink out of a golden goblet. He wanted to be a frog. He liked
being a frog. Besides, now that he was a prince, the lily leaf had
collapsed under his weight, and there he was, up to his neck in
green slime – which is all very well for a frog, but not very
comfortable for a prince in a velvet suit.

So he clambered out of the pond and looked round for the witch
who had enchanted him. She was sitting under a willow tree,
looking rather pleased with herself, because it was the first time
she had ever done such a thing. "Well, Frogmorton," she said.
"How do you like being a prince?"

The prince shivered. "I don't like it at all," he replied. "Turn
me back into a frog immediately."

"I can't do that," said the witch, making excuses. "You must be
a prince for at least an hour before I can turn you into anything
else. Anyhow," she went on, "I thought you'd be pleased to be a
prince instead of an ugly green frog."

Frogmorton was offended. "I wasn't ugly," he retorted. "In
fact, as frogs go, I was considered rather handsome."

"That's as may be," said the witch, "but I think you're far more
handsome as a prince. I've gone to a great deal of trouble to turn you
into a prince, and I've even provided you with a beautiful princess
to be your wife and live with you in your castle." She clapped her
hands, and there stood a princess with long golden hair.

Frogmorton sniffed. He didn't like the look of her at all. She
wasn't a bit like a frog and her hair was a horrid colour. "I'm
catching a cold," he said. "It's these wet clothes I'm wearing. You
must make me a fire so that I can dry out my cloak."

"Make your own fire," mocked the witch, who was very displeased with Frogmorton for not liking her spell.

"I don't know how to do it," said Frogmorton, sneezing.

"You do it by magic," said the witch.

"I can't do any magic," Frogmorton responded, at which the princess burst into tears, for she, too, seemed to be rather wet and cold.

The princess's tears seemed to disturb the witch, for she suddenly said, "Oh, very well. Come over here and I will whisper the magic word that makes fire."

Frogmorton went over to the witch and she whispered in his ear the magic word for fire-making. Only princes who have been frogs and witches who have turned them into frogs are allowed to know that word; otherwise, it would be too dangerous. That is why it has to be whispered instead of said out loud.

Frogmorton whispered the magic word into his cupped hands, and in no time at all he had a blazing fire. "Now," he said, "I want a blanket to wear whilst my clothes are drying."

"So do I," wailed the princess.

"Tell me the magic word for making blankets," demanded the prince, looking hard at the witch.

Now, of all things in the world, the one thing that that witch couldn't do was make magic blankets. She knew the word all right, because she had read it in her magic book of spells, which she had had for her five-hundredth birthday, but she didn't know how to pronounce it. She had tried several times, but every time she had got it wrong, and instead of blankets she had made frying pans and cricket bats and things like that. "I can't tell you the magic word," she said, sulkily.

"Why not?" asked Frogmorton.

"Because it is beyond the power of the human tongue to say it."

"Maybe I could say it," Frogmorton suggested, "because I can still say all my froggy words."

The witch sneered. "You think you're very clever, don't you?" she said. "But you won't succeed. I have been trying for years to make magic blankets, but I have never succeeded. However, as you are so determined to make a fool of yourself, do try. The word is spelt SZQUGYX."

"That's easy," said the prince, who still had a tongue like a frog because the witch had made a mistake; and he said the word twice into his cupped hands.

Immediately two blankets came floating down out of the sky. One fell on to the shoulders of the princess and the other on the head of Frogmorton. They were beautiful blankets. They had blue stars around the edges and they were made of bumbledown and fross. Anyone who could learn to say that magic word could make a fortune.

But the witch wasn't pleased at all. She jumped up and down with anger, shaking her fist as witches are inclined to do, and told Frogmorton that she would never, ever, turn him back into a frog again. At this the princess wailed louder than ever, and the prince went over to her to comfort her. "I'll make a bargain with you," he said to the witch over his shoulder.

"Who are you to bargain with me?" she screeched. "You're only a miserable frog in disguise. I'll have none of your bargains, and if you try to be too clever with me I'll turn you into a broomstick and fly off with you to the north pole!"

"I was only going to say that I could teach you how to say the magic word for making blankets," he said quietly, "but if you're not interested . . ."

The witch interrupted him. "You couldn't do it," she said.

"Oh yes I could."

"Prove it," said the witch.

By this time a great many woodland creatures had gathered around to see what was going on over by the pool, and they all cried out, "Yes, yes, prove it, prove it!"

"As soon as you turn me into a frog again," said Frogmorton.

"I won't do that," snapped the witch, running off and disappearing in the trees.

Frogmorton sighed. "We shall have to make the best of it," he said to the princess, who was gazing into the deep brown water of the pool and almost making it flood over, so many tears was she shedding. Frogmorton took off his wet clothes and put on his magic blanket and turned his back politely whilst the princess did the same. Soon they were warm, but still not very happy. The prince didn't like the princess's pink and white skin, and she was horrified by his tiny feet, because, of course, the truth was that she, too, had been a frog.

They had been sitting by the fire for a long time when the witch came back. All the woodland creatures gave a cheer when they saw her, because they had become very bored with nothing exciting happening. The witch didn't admit it, but she had been to consult her mother, who was a very old witch indeed, about nine hundred and ten years old, and although she couldn't make magic blankets, either, she did know how to turn a prince back into a frog. "I've decided to do as you ask," said the witch.

Frogmorton sprang to his feet. "You'll turn me back into a frog?" he cried in delight.

"If you will keep your part of the bargain."

"Will you make the princess into a frog as well?" he demanded.

"Oh, very well," said the witch, very ungraciously. She took a deep breath and did exactly as her mother had told her. (Any girl whose name begins with a B or an S can do it quite as easily if she really tries.) She walked about in a mysterious pattern, counting her footsteps and muttering strange words, and quite suddenly Frogmorton and the princess were frogs again, sitting on the same lily leaf, holding hands.

It was lovely. They wiggled their toes in the water and nibbled the same bit of pond weed, and felt beautifully squishy and slimy again.

"The magic word!" hissed the witch, coming close to the pond. "Teach me how to say it."

Frogmorton croaked, and the princess croaked, and although they both pronounced the word perfectly the witch didn't seem able to imitate it. The strange thing was that, now they were frogs again, the magic word didn't bring any more magic blankets, and every time the witch tried to imitate the sound, she only got frying pans that bonked her on the head.

So, if ever you are walking through a wood, and you see an old woman sitting beside a pool trying to imitate the croaking of a frog, you'd better turn round and run as fast as you can in the opposite direction. Especially if she's surrounded by frying pans.

*   *   *

Follow-up Discussion

This story contains three or four moral issues and these can be emphasized at the end.

Frogmorton shows consideration for others and even the "wicked" witch is moved by the princess's tears. When it becomes clear that the witch is not going to turn them back into frogs, the princess and Frogmorton decide to be satisfied and make the most of the situation. Caring and sharing is another moral point that this story raises. All these points could form the basis for discussion after the story.

Language Development and Creative Writing
The witch with her spells provides the opportunity for making up some magic words. This can be developed into tongue twisters, both recognized examples and those made up by the children.

Environmental Studies and Science
This is an ideal story for use at the time when ponds contain frog spawn. It leads naturally into an in-depth study into the life cycle of the frog. It could broaden out into an ecological study of a pond.

The touch of the green slime suggests a project on the senses, in particular the sense of touch.

Art and Craft
Pictures and models of frogs would be a natural progression into the creative activities.

Drama
This story can be adapted for dramatization, but it might have more impact if it were read to the children by a teacher.

Ferdinand, Felipe and Fandango

(Teamwork, Politeness, Consideration for Others)

A long time ago there lived three frogs. Their names were Ferdinand, Felipe and Fandango. They lived in a well.

Ferdinand, Felipe and Fandango were very good friends. They did everything together. They swam together. They slept together. They ate together. And they were always polite to each other.

One day they decided to go for a hop together. (Frogs don't go for walks, of course, because their legs are the wrong shape.) They hopped out of the well. They hopped across the grass.

"This is a beautiful place," said Fandango, looking round.

"It is indeed," said Ferdinand.

"We have never hopped so far before," said Felipe.

They now saw that their well was situated in the garden of a palace. All around them were flowers and fountains and hedges cut into fantastic shapes. It was the most beautiful place they had ever dreamed of.

"Just fancy our living in the well all that time," said Fandango, "and never knowing that our surroundings were like this."

The other two frogs agreed. "And if we are so happy living in our well," said Ferdinand, "just think how contented the people who live in the palace must be."

"And all the creatures that live in the gardens," said Felipe.

He had no sooner finished speaking than they heard a terrible cry. The three frogs hopped quickly into the shelter of a bush to watch out for the creature that was making the noise.

It was a peacock. His magnificent tail was spread like a fan and the feathers on top of his head were standing erect. He was having a dreadful quarrel with another peacock. They were pecking at each other and saying the rudest things imaginable.

The frogs were horrified at the behaviour of the peacocks and they took the first opportunity of hopping away from them. After a short time they spied four Siamese cats prowling about along a terrace near the palace.

Suddenly one cat sprang at another, and in no time at all the four beautiful animals were snarling and scratching and spitting at one another as if they were trying to put an end to themselves. The three frogs were quite dismayed. Shaking their heads sadly they went on their way.

The next thing that they saw was a huge cage in which several monkeys were throwing themselves about and generally behaving in a most objectionable manner. The three frogs sighed and decided to go back home.

Now in the palace there lived a young king. He had come from a land far across the sea, and because everything was new and strange to him he was keeping his mind occupied by decorating his new palace.

He had had his young queen's rooms painted with a design of flowers and fruit. The Council Chamber he had hung with portraits of his ancestors. The splendid hall was so full of pictures of beautiful ladies that even his crotchety old Prime Minister was so shy that he couldn't walk through it.

Now he was trying to think of something to paint on the ceiling of his Throne Room. He went out into the garden with his young queen on his arm. "What *shall* it be, Nelly?" he said. (Although her name was Eleanor Jane he always called her Nelly because it was easier to remember.)

He looked at the tame monkeys in their big cage. They were throwing bananas and spitting peanuts at one another. He couldn't paint *that* on his ceiling.

He watched the peacocks tearing their feathers out and shrieking until their big toes quivered. He couldn't paint *that* on his ceiling, either.

He saw the Siamese cats all rolled up together in one huge ball of fur. How could he show such a thing in his Throne Room?

And then Queen Nelly caught sight of the frogs making their way back to their well. "Let's follow them," she whispered, "and see what they do."

Ferdinand, Felipe and Fandango were so anxious to get away from all the horrid things that they had seen that they didn't notice the young king and queen following them. They proceeded towards the well in the most orderly manner imaginable.

When they reached the edge of the well Felipe stood back and bowed. "After you, my dear friends," he said.

"Thank you, Felipe," said Fandango. "Perhaps we could go for a hop together tomorrow?"

"That would be very pleasant," said Felipe.

Fandango plunged into the water.

"Thank you for the pleasure of your company, Felipe," said Ferdinand, bowing. "Perhaps you will have supper with me tonight?"

"I should enjoy that very much indeed," said Felipe.

And they jumped into the well together.

A few weeks later a visitor to the palace was received in the Throne Room by the young king and queen. "Tell me," said the visitor, "why you have painted frogs on the ceiling of this room. Surely you could have portrayed a more noble group of animals?"

The young king smiled. "I don't think I could," he said.

And with that the visitor had to be content.

*   *   *

Follow-up Discussion

I am sure most teachers will have experienced occasions when children come to them claiming that "Johnny hit me" or "Mary's fallen out with me". This is part of school life. However, there are times when this almost reaches epidemic proportions and it is for just these situations that this story seems designed.

If the children can relate the pain they suffer, both physical and emotional, when they fight or squabble, to the antics of the peacocks, the Siamese cats and the frogs, they will be closer to the realization that politeness and consideration are completely painless.

Language Development and Creative Writing

The peacock is a beautiful bird with a horrendous shriek. The Siamese cat is a proud animal with a very savage streak. The monkey is noted for its amusing antics, but it is quite capable of being objectionable. On the other hand, the frog is regarded by some people as being ugly and not very nice to touch. These characteristics pose the question: "Are things always as they first appear?" This is a discussion point that can be developed for language and creative writing. It may help children to understand that the appearance of physically handicapped people should not be a reason for shying away from them. Their personality should be given some important consideration.

Environmental Studies and Science
The common frog has only got its ugly appearance as a defence mechanism, but is really quite harmless, whilst some very beautiful things, like Venus's fly trap, are quite deadly. This story can be used to launch a project into the various functions played in nature by colour. The children can classify animals and plants according to the functions of their colouration.

Art and Craft
Paintings of the animals and plants the children have studied in the environmental studies project would make an attractive means of recording the findings. The children could make masks for the animals from the story.

Drama and Movement
Using the masks, this story can be made into an attractive play for assembly.

The animals in the story display different characteristics which the children can explore in a movement lesson.

The Special Friends

(Loyalty)

One night when George the hedgehog went out in search of his supper he met a one-eyed rabbit. He was going to walk straight by him when the one-eyed rabbit said, "Won't you stop for a few moments and talk to me?"

George's heart gave a little jump. "You want to talk to *me*?" he asked in amazement.

"Yes, please," said the one-eyed rabbit.

"Why?" asked George.

"Because I have nobody else in the whole wide world to talk to," said the one-eyed rabbit. "Nobody."

"Neither have I," cried George. "There are no other hedgehogs around here and all the other animals say I am much too prickly to be their friend. I don't know why they should say that, because underneath I'm not prickly at all."

The one-eyed rabbit began to look excited. "If you haven't got a friend," he said, "will you let me be your friend? I don't mind a bit about your being prickly. My name is Hugo. Do let me be your friend."

So the two animals became the best of friends. Every night they would meet and have supper together, and when they had eaten their fill they would sit in the grass together and watch the moon. Sometimes they would tell stories. Sometimes they would sing. Often they would just sit there doing nothing at all, just happy to be together, because they were friends.

One night, as George was going towards their usual meeting place, he met a small brown mouse, who said, "Are you going anywhere special, hedgehog? I arranged to meet my friend here to go looking for adventures, but as he hasn't kept the appointment would you care to go with me instead?"

Now it so happened that George had always secretly longed to go and seek adventure, but he had never been brave enough to go alone. How wonderful it would be to go with this new acquaintance, who, judging by his manner, seemed to be brave enough for both of them! "I should be delighted to come with you," he said, "but I have arranged to meet my special friend, the one-eyed rabbit. You wouldn't mind if he came along with us, too, would you?"

"Mind?" shrieked the mouse. "Of course I should mind. I'm not accustomed to being seen in the company of one-eyed rabbits. So make up your mind. If you come with me, you come alone."

George detained the mouse a little longer. "My friend Hugo is waiting for me," he said. "It wouldn't be kind to keep him waiting for me all night without letting him know where I am. Surely you can understand that?"

"What an old-fashioned idea!" laughed the mouse. "Your friend won't mind if you don't meet him. He'll soon find somebody else."

"But he won't!" cried George. "I'm the only friend he has in the whole wide world, and I can't keep him waiting all night. Besides," he added, "I'm not ashamed of his being a one-eyed rabbit, and I think it's unfair of you to say he can't come along just because he is."

"Very well," snapped the mouse, "if that's the way you feel about it I'll go and find someone else to share my adventures with." And away he went.

George continued on his way.

Down on the common Hugo was waiting for his friend George to arrive. Usually it was very quiet on the common, which was the reason why it had been chosen as their meeting place, but tonight Hugo thought he could hear a lot of snuffling and whispering going on. He didn't actually see anyone, however, until a huge toad came leaping up to him and said, "Hullo, one-eyed rabbit! All on your own? How would you like to come with me on a bold adventure? Just the two of us, all expenses shared."

"Oh," cried Hugo, "I should like that above everything, except being with my special friend. I'm sure he should be here at any moment, so if you will just wait until he arrives we can all go together."

"Who is your special friend?" asked the toad.

"George the hedgehog," said Hugo.

"What?" croaked the toad. "Me make a friend of a prickly hedgehog? Not likely! You'd better come with me now, before he arrives, and then he will think you've been unavoidably prevented from meeting him."

"I couldn't do that," said Hugo. "He's the only friend I've got."

"No he isn't," the toad reminded him. "I'm your friend now, but I won't go anywhere in the company of a hedgehog, so take it or leave it. Come with me or wait for him."

"I shall wait for George," said Hugo loyally. "He was my friend when nobody else wanted me."

"What a silly thing to say," grumbled the toad. "Nobody bothers about that sort of thing nowadays. It's every man for himself."

"I think you're wrong," said Hugo, "and I'm going to wait for my special friend."

The toad made a grunting noise in his throat and jumped away into the darkness.

When the two friends met, neither of them told the other about their encounter. They ate their supper and then sat side by side as usual to talk.

"I say, George," said Hugo after a while, "is it my imagination or can I really hear strange noises all around us tonight?"

"I was just going to ask you the same thing myself," responded George. "I've had the most curious feeling all night that we were being watched."

Hugo shivered. "I hope it isn't the hunters," he said. "Perhaps we'd better go and find a nice safe hole somewhere in which to hide."

They were just about to go when out of the darkness, from all directions, there came a crowd of animals, all the wild creatures imaginable, large and small. George was so afraid that he rolled himself up into a ball in the way that hedgehogs do, but Hugo could only think of covering up his one eye and trembling until his teeth chattered.

The animals crowded round them, and formed a circle. Among them were the brown mouse and the toad. "Don't be afraid," said the mouse. "We don't want to hurt you."

Hugo uncovered his one eye. "What do you want?" he asked.

"We want to be your friends," said the mouse.

George uncurled himself and looked at the animals. "All of you?" he asked in astonishment. "You all want us to be your friends?"

"Yes, please," cried the animals, and then the mouse came

forward and spoke alone. "This is the way it was," he said. "Two or three of us – all good friends – decided to go off and look for adventure, but we met with so many difficulties on the way that we thought it would be a good idea to ask some other animals to join us. Lots of them did, but after a while they began to let us down; other interests diverted them; they became disloyal and one of them even betrayed us to an enemy. So we formed a plan. We decided to test those whom we asked to join us. And both of you have passed the test of loyalty."

"Do you mean that we can still come with you to look for adventure?" cried Hugo. "Both of us?"

"If you will," returned the mouse, "we shall be glad of your company."

So many friends! Hugo and George could hardly believe it. They set off that very night and did, indeed, find many adventures, all of which they tackled together. But two of the animals still shared a very special friendship, and their names were – yes, Hugo and George.

*   *   *

Follow-up Discussion
The story should be preceded by a discussion and explanation of loyalty and betrayal. The children could possibly give examples of both.

The follow-up discussion should indicate that the children now have a better understanding of the meanings of loyalty and betrayal. Friendship is one of the most valuable things in the world and loyalty is the most important aspect of real friendship.

Another important discussion point brought out in the story is that disability does not affect a person's ability to form relationships with others. The children must learn to accept people who have a disability.

Language Development and Creative Writing
The children could talk or write about their best friend, giving as accurate a description as possible but without naming the person. The other children could try to work out who it is from the evidence provided.

Environmental Studies and Science
The animals mentioned in the story could be studied, their habitats, food, life cycle and hibernation patterns. The rabbit, the hedgehog, the mouse and the toad are mentioned specifically. They would live in harmony. What other animals do the children think would be in the crowd that

surrounded George and Hugo? They would have to be able to distinguish between those animals that would be compatible and the animals of prey that would hunt them.

Art and Craft
Models can be made of most of the animals mentioned in the story, using a variety of media. The hedgehog can be made from a large potato and cocktail sticks. The mouse, the rabbit and the toad can be made with clay or papier-mâché.

Drama, Movement and Music
Using masks, the children can dramatize this story for assembly.

The different animal movements could form the theme for a drama and movement lesson. The mouse would scuttle, the hedgehog scurry, the rabbit and toad hop.

There are numerous songs that can be used in connection with this story.

The Beetle Who Lived in a Bottle

(Helpfulness, Kindness)

The beetle who lived in a bottle was carrying home his shopping. The day was hot and his way lay uphill, so the beetle was very tired. Halfway up the hill he saw the worm who lived in a walnut.

"Good morning, worm," he said. "Please will you help me to carry my shopping back home?"

"Certainly not," responded the worm. "I am far too busy cleaning my house before I go out this afternoon. I have been told that there is to be a party and I mean to be there."

"Hum," said the beetle. "Do you happen to know who is giving the party? I should dearly like to be there myself, but if I don't get my shopping back home I never shall be."

"I don't know who is giving the party," replied the worm, "for the invitation has not yet arrived, but I am sure that *I* shall receive one."

"I hope you do," said the beetle as he toiled on.

Before very long he came to the door of the spider who lived in a sponge. He knocked on the door. "Good morning, spider," he called. "I know you're in there. Won't you come out and give me a hand with my parcels? I can't manage them all by myself."

"Hee, hee!" giggled the spider. "You shouldn't have bought so many, then, should you? I have some spinning to do before I can come out. I expect to receive an invitation to a party before very long."

"Hum," said the beetle, "and do you know whose party it is? I should like to be there, too, but I must get my shopping home first."

"Oh, *that* doesn't matter," responded the spider, "as long as I get *my* invitation."

"I hope you do," said the beetle, and looked around for other assistance.

Sitting in the shade was the maggot who lived in a mushroom.

"Good morning, maggot," said the beetle. "I know you are not at all fond of the sun, but I should be much obliged if you would give me a little help with my shopping, just to the top of the hill."

The maggot remained where he was. "I'm resting," he said. "I expect to be called to a party this afternoon, and I want to be fresh for the dancing. I can't spare the time to help you."

"Hum," said the beetle. "I want to be at the party, too. Do you know where it is to be held?"

"Oh no," said the maggot. "I haven't been told, but I'm always invited to every party that's held around here, so I expect I shall find out very soon."

"I hope you do," said the beetle.

He struggled along for a little way and stopped to rest beside a large brown apple. "Good morning, beetle," cried the ants who lived in the apple. "You have a long way to go and your parcels seem heavy. Can we help you to carry them home?"

The beetle who lived in the bottle said, "Thankyou, ants, but aren't you getting ready for the party this afternoon?"

"Oh, we don't expect to be invited," said the ants. "There are far too many of us. If we all turned up at the party there wouldn't be room for anybody else."

"Then you *shall* come!" cried the beetle. "It is my party. I have been out shopping for everything I need, but nobody would help me to carry it home until I met you."

So the ants picked up the parcels and carried them all the way to the top of the hill. One by one, they crept into the bottle until there was no room for anybody else. Then the beetle shut the door and they had a wonderful time. The worm who lived in the walnut and the spider who lived in the sponge and the maggot who lived in the mushroom went out to see who was giving the party. But when they got there, all they could do was watch from outside as the beetle who lived in the bottle and all his friends danced the night away.

*   *   *

Follow-up Discussion
There are several aspects of this story that can be developed into discussion points. It raises the questions of helpfulness, kindness, Who is my neighbour?, and "As ye sow, so shall ye reap".

The story of the Good Samaritan is a biblical parallel that can be used alongside this story. One question raised by the story is "Should the beetle expect help without offering something in return?" He only reciprocates with the invitation to the party when the ants help him with his shopping.

Language Development and Creative Writing
The children could be encouraged to think of rhyming names for all the mini-beasts mentioned in the story. Names that are appropriate to the lifestyle or the way the creature moves would be an extension of this activity.

Environmental Studies and Science
The story suggests a research project into mini-beasts. In the case of the maggot, there is the question of metamorphosis and life cycles. All the creatures mentioned in the story are part of the diet of other animals, which introduces the children to food chains.

Art and Craft
The story provides the opportunity for painting a spider's web pattern, or patterns with the shapes of a worm's movement.

Drama, Movement and Music
The older children could make models of the creatures that feature in the story. These could then be adapted for use in a puppet play to be performed for the younger children. The sound effects could be produced using tuned and untuned percussion instruments.

The Cat Who Stared

(Consideration for Others, Kindness to Animals)

Once there was a farmer who was cruel to his animals. He beat the donkey, he kicked the cat, he yelled at the cows, and he would never let the dogs come into the kitchen, not even on the stormiest night.

His wife was a gentle creature, and she often remonstrated with him over his conduct towards the animals, but all he said was, "They're only animals. They don't mind."

But the animals *did* mind, and one day they decided to do something about it. The cat, who was very good at staring at people until she put an idea into their heads, sat on the sill outside the window and stared in at the farmer's wife. Soon, the farmer's wife said, "I'll go and pick some mushrooms for supper," but she didn't suspect that it was the cat who had put the idea into her head.

"Be careful what you're about," said the farmer. "Don't go picking any toadstools instead."

"Of course not," said the farmer's wife.

The cat went with her and stared at her until she picked the one mushroom that wasn't a mushroom at all, but something that only animals know about. When it was cooked and the farmer had eaten it, he began to understand what the animals were saying.

"You're a cruel and ignorant man," said the cat, as he kicked her out of the way.

"That cat has far too much to say for itself," said the farmer to his wife. At least, that is what he *thought* he was saying, but to his wife it sounded like "Miaow!"

He went into the yard, where the dogs were trying to shelter from the rain. They looked at him with their brown eyes and said, "Have you no feelings for our predicament, you selfish, bad-tempered man?"

"Those dogs have far too much to say for themselves," said the farmer again, but this time it sounded like "Woof, woof!"

The cows were waiting to be milked, but the farmer angrily pushed them aside. They said, "Heartless, unfeeling brute that you are – can't you see that we have feelings, just like people?"

"Those cows have far too much to say for themselves," the farmer shouted, but all that came out of his mouth was "Moo! Moo!"

Then he went to harness the donkey to his cart, but the donkey was tired after working in the fields all day, and she fell down in exhaustion. The farmer took a stick and began to beat her until she struggled to her feet. "Oh cruel master!" she cried. "I must have rest."

"This stupid donkey has far too much to say for itself," growled the farmer, but it sounded more like "Ee-aw, ee-aw!"

The farmer's wife rushed indoors and locked herself in. "He's gone quite mad!" she said to herself as he pleaded to be let in, for all *she* could hear was, "Miaow, woof-woof, moo-moo, ee-aw" – and that didn't mean anything to her. She waited until her husband had gone into the barn to shelter from the rain, and she crept across the yard and locked him in. She wouldn't let him out for anything.

After a while the farmer's wife became so lonely on her own that she let in the dogs to sleep on the rug, and allowed the donkey to rest in the yard, and she sang to the cows when she milked them, which they liked very much indeed.

As for the cat – well, I think you can guess what the cat did. She stared and she stared at the farmer's wife and she put this idea into her head: "Your husband has far too much to say for himself, but until you can understand what he says you must *never* allow him to come into the house again."

And she never did.

*   *   *

Follow-up Discussion
This story should lead naturally into discussion about cruelty to animals. It might be useful to use the story either just before or just after Christmas, since this is a time when children are given pets, particularly puppies, many of which end up in animal shelters having been abandoned.

The farmer in this story was particularly cruel, but there are aspects of any farmer's attitudes to animals that non-agricultural people might regard as cruel, whilst in reality they are not. For instance, most farmers do not keep working dogs in the house. The children could consider and discuss why they think this is the case.

Language Development and Creative Writing

The children could work as a group to make up some poetry based on animal sounds.

Another possible line for development in language and creative writing could be to ask the children to imagine that they have magical powers. They can think of and discuss the ways in which they would repay people who are cruel to animals.

Environmental Studies and Science

This story opens up the opportunity for the children to do an in-depth study into farming. The farmer in the story was cruel to his animals, which would not make for good husbandry. The children could research methods that would help to produce a good milk yield or egg laying.

Art and Craft

The children could make a model farm with all the animals. They could paint pictures of farm animals.

Drama

The story would probably have greater impact on the children if it were read to the assembly or class.

Fine Feathers

(Cheerfulness in Adversity, Concern for the Environment)

Seppy the house sparrow flew to the tree where his mother and father were preening themselves in the summer sunshine. "It isn't fair!" he burst out indignantly, flapping his wings so fast that he almost knocked his poor mother off the branch.

"Do be careful, Seppy," said his father sternly. "Now tell me – what isn't fair?"

"I've just been into the garden next door," said Seppy, "and there's a bird over there with red feathers underneath his chin and all down his breast."

"Well," said his father, "go on."

"That's it," went on Seppy. "That's what isn't fair."

His mother stopped what she was doing for a moment and said, "Do you mean it isn't fair that he's got red feathers and you haven't?"

Seppy gave an indignant chirp and nodded his head.

"He must be a robin," said his father. "Robins do have red feathers. There's nothing you can do about that."

"But I *want* red feathers," Seppy broke in sulkily. "Why should he have them and not me?"

"I told you," responded his father, "because he's a robin."

Seppy's mother looked at him in surprise. "You are a house sparrow," she told him. "House sparrows don't have red feathers, so you may as well stop worrying about it. For my part I much prefer brown. Far less flamboyant and pretentious, you know."

"Why don't you go and find something tasty to eat?" laughed his father. "You'll soon forget about red feathers."

"I'm not hungry," snapped Seppy, and he flew into the next tree to be miserable all by himself.

"That boy," said his father, looking across at him, "doesn't know when he's well off. After all, he might have done so much worse. He might have been born a bald eagle, and *then* he would have had something to complain about." And he roared with laughter at his own joke.

Seppy had tucked his head into his feathers and was muttering to himself, when all of a sudden he became aware that somebody had come and perched near him on the branch. He raised his head, thinking that it might be his mother, but it wasn't.

Seppy's eyes widened in amazement and envy. The robin was forgotten. The bird beside him was a mixture of the most gorgeous colours that Seppy had ever seen – yellow, and blue and whitey-green – and it seemed to Seppy the most desirable thing in the world to have feathers like that.

"Good morning," said the blue tit. "Nice weather, isn't it?"

Seppy was so jealous that he couldn't reply. He flew away into a nearby bush and stamped his feet and flicked his tail angrily up and down.

"What's the matter?" enquired a tiny voice close at hand, and when Seppy turned around he saw a cheeky little bird who was quite drab compared with the robin and the blue tit, so he replied, "Nothing much. I just feel miserable, that's all."

"On such a lovely day?" returned the wren, putting her head on one side and regarding him with great curiosity. "Why do you feel miserable when the sun is shining and there's food for everyone? You should have been here last winter, and then you would have had something to be miserable about, I can tell you." All the same, she looked quite sympathetic, so Seppy gave an exaggerated sigh and decided to confide in her.

"I feel so shabby," he said. "Some of the other birds have got beautiful coloured feathers all over themselves, and I've only got brown. It isn't fair."

The wren looked rather complacent. "I don't see anything wrong with having plain brown feathers," she said. "I think they're very attractive." She fluffed out her own for a moment and then went on, "Anyhow, it has its advantages. I like to lead a quiet life. I don't like people staring at me. Think how difficult it must be for the robin to hide himself away when people will watch him all the time. I shouldn't like that at all."

Seppy saw that he was going to get no consolation from the wren, so he said rather rudely, "Why don't you go away and let me mope on my own?"

"Very well," said the wren, "if that's what you want." And away she flew.

It was now midday and the sun was at its hottest. Seppy decided to go and find some water to bathe in. He thought he could hear the sound of a stream nearby, so he flew towards it. He was pleasantly surprised. The stream was dark and deep, flowing through sandy banks, and in the middle of the stream was a large flat stone with a hollow in the middle, just right for bathing. Seppy alighted on an overhanging branch and, in the manner of all birds, looked carefully all around for signs of life. Just for a moment he knew that the wren was right about being inconspicuous. Sitting quite still on the branch he seemed to merge with the shadows of the leaves.

After a while he relaxed. There were no enemies here. He was just about to fly down to the bathing place when a brilliant flash of blue-green light seemed to dart into the water. A moment later he saw that it was a bird. Oh, such a bird! He had never seen anything so beautiful in his life. It was true that the bird was larger than himself, and that he had a very short tail and a rather large head with a long beak, but that didn't matter beside the gorgeous colouring of his feathers. He had a fish in his beak. As Seppy watched, the bird disappeared into a dark hole in the river bank.

Seppy was transfixed. He had no heart left to go bathing. He simply sat there moping, wondering how he could acquire bright feathers. Was it perhaps something that the birds *ate* that made them so brightly-coloured? If he dived into the water, caught a fish and ate it, would his feathers change colour?

A voice behind him said, "Going in?"

"In?" said Seppy, vaguely, throwing a look at the dark hole.

"In the pool," was the response.

"No," said Seppy.

"Then if it's all the same to you," went on the voice, "I will."

"Go ahead," said Seppy, without much interest.

The bird flew down into the pool. Seppy continued to gaze at the hole into which the beautiful bird had flown, but after a few moments the gurgles and splashes and gargles of the bird in the water made him turn and look. "What a handsome bird!" he thought, as the bather emerged from the water and shook out his feathers so that they gleamed in the bright sunshine. It wasn't so much that he was brightly-coloured as that his feathers seemed to blend so well together. Deep rich chestnut, and white, and a black bib, with a grey cap on his head. A bright eye with a little white stripe, and a compact little beak. As the bird smoothed down his feathers Seppy was surprised to see that he looked very much like his father. He had never thought about his father being a handsome bird.

"Why don't you go in?" enquired the stranger. "The water's just right. Nice and warm."

"What's the point?" grumbled Seppy. "Nothing I can do will make me as handsome as any of the other birds I've seen this morning."

"What makes you say that?" demanded the stranger. "I know you're still very young, but it seems to me that you're coming along very nicely – very nicely indeed."

"What do you mean?" asked Seppy.

"Well, you'll soon have your adult feathers," the other replied.

Seppy's heart gave a little leap. "Do you mean to say that my feathers are going to change colour?" he cried. "And can I have any colour I like?"

"Well, I wouldn't say that," laughed the other bird. "Would you settle for a suit like mine?"

"Oh yes!" said Seppy.

"Then I think it's very likely that you soon will have," was the response, "because you're a house sparrow like me."

Without another word Seppy plunged into the water. He was going to grow new feathers! And, after all, brown was as good a colour as any. As he threw the water over himself he listened to what the other bird was saying. It was almost like a song. "I'm a sparrow, I'm a sparrow, I'm a sparrow."

Seppy hopped out of the water. "Not a robin, not a wren," he chuckled, "but a sparrow."

His new friend clapped him on the back. "Feel better now?" he asked.

"Oh yes," replied Seppy, "much better."

And in no time at all they had made up a little song which they sang together:

I'm a sparrow, I'm a sparrow, I'm a sparrow,
Not a robin, not a wren, but a sparrow,
And I'm proud of every feather,
So we'll sing it both together,
I'm a sparrow, I'm a sparrow, I'm a sparrow.

All the sparrows for miles around heard the song, and they all came to see what was going on. Before long they were all singing.

> I'm a sparrow, I'm a sparrow, I'm a sparrow,
> Not a starling, not a swan, but a sparrow,
> And we'll sing it all together
> In the balmy summer weather,
> I'm a sparrow, I'm a sparrow, I'm a sparrow.

* * *

Follow-up Discussion
The discussion that should follow this story can be based on the principle that we all have our saving grace and do not need to be envious of others.

The teacher leading the discussion could profitably emphasize this by quoting examples from within the assembled company. It would provide an opportunity for highlighting the qualities of some of the more unfortunate children who come in for ridicule from the other members of the group.

Language Development and Creative Writing
The songs of many birds have been likened to human speech – for example, the chaffinch is heard to be saying, "pink, pink", the great tit "teacher, teacher" and the lapwing's cry gives the bird its vernacular English name, "peewit". More extensively, the yellow hammer is supposed to say "a little bit of bread and no cheese" and the wood pigeon "here come two coos". This could be used in a language development lesson.

Environmental Studies and Science
The story provides a stimulus for an extensive study on the theme of birds. This is a subject that can be profitably pursued by both rural and urban schools. A bird table, bird boxes, and even a bird-watching hide can be constructed quite easily and cheaply. Observation records of behaviour, colours of feathers, nesting places and materials can be a rewarding activity. Studying bird populations can bring in mathematical activities, such as tallying and graphical representation.

Art and Craft
Paintings of birds provide the opportunity for the use of a wide range of colours. Models can be made of different birds. The robin is a territorial bird who will defend his territory from other robins with ferocity. They have even been known to attack a model robin placed in their territory. The children may be lucky enough to observe this.

Drama and Movement
This is quite a difficult story to dramatize, but there are aspects of the
story that could be used in a movement lesson. Observation of birds on
the ground will reveal that different birds move in different ways. The
children could copy the movement of each species observed.

The Teddy Bears' Picnic

(Helpfulness, Caring and Sharing, Teamwork)

It was the night of the teddy bears' picnic, and as it *never* rains on the night of the teddy bears' picnic, they were all looking forward to having a good time.

The place where the picnic is held is the secret wood midway between here and halfway in between, and on that particular night there seemed to be more teddy bears gathering there than ever before.

The conversations were something like this:

"Good evening. Lovely night for the picnic, isn't it?"

"Absolutely perfect. Let me see – it's Teddy Bear Jones, isn't it?"

"That's right. And if I remember rightly you are Teddy Bear Twistle. I never forget a face."

"Nor do I. Well, how have things been going with you since last year? Treating you well at the Jones's are they?"

"Can't complain. I get pushed out of bed in the middle of the night quite often, but then who doesn't? Young Roderick's very good to me on the whole. What about you?"

Teddy Bear Twistle, who was asked this question, looked rather embarrassed. He lowered his voice to a whisper and replied, "Well, the fact is, old man, that I have a bit of a problem."

"Oh?" said Teddy Bear Jones. "What is it?"

"Well, I don't know if you will understand, always having had a boy owner, but my owner is a girl, and girls do tend rather to want to put – to put ribbons around a fellow's neck."

"Oh dear," said Teddy Bear Jones, "I don't think I should care for that."

"It wouldn't be too bad," went on his friend, "if she didn't tie them quite so tightly. Sometimes I think she will choke me. She's a nice little girl, but very strong, and she ties such good knots – I thought I should never get the knots undone in time to come out tonight, for you see I couldn't come to the party in a pink ribbon, could I?"

Underneath a nearby maple tree two more old friends had met.

"You're looking very well," said Teddy Bear Johnson.

"You look quite fit yourself," responded Teddy Bear Smythe, clapping him on the shoulder. "Still got both your eyes I see. It's always the eyes that are the first to go. They don't fix them the way they used to do in our day. Why –" he leaned forward and spoke confidentially so as not to offend anyone who might be listening, "– I've even heard of them being *stuck* on with glue sometimes, instead of the good old hook and bar arrangement. What do you think of that?"

"Terrible," said Teddy Bear Johnson, shaking his head. "Did you hear about poor old Teddy Bear Bagley? Had his hair cut by *his* owner, and it doesn't grown again, you know. He was asking me if I knew of anybody who made Teddy Bear wigs, but I couldn't help him there."

At that moment Big Bear Teddy Bear, who was the chief bear for that year, called attention and said that the food was all ready if they would kindly step that way. All the teddy bears lined up and passed one by one through the gap between the brambles to the glade where the picnic was spread out. There were gasps of delight.

"Oh, what a feast!"

"Better than ever before."

"My favourite sandwiches!"

"Gingerbread bears!"

Each of the teddy bears took a plate and helped himself to whatever he fancied. All this time there had been a *little* teddy bear running anxiously from group to group asking a particular question. At last he came to the spot where Teddy Bear Jones and his friends were chatting and eating together.

"Can you tell me, please – please – if any of you have seen Teddy Bear Taylor tonight? I've looked everywhere for him. He *never* misses the picnic; it's the only thing he looks forward to every year, far more than his annual trip to the seaside or Granny Taylor's birthday, or anything. And he isn't here! Don't you see, he isn't here! I'm sure something must have happened to him on the way!" And he wiped a tear from his eye.

Teddy Bear Twistle patted him on the head. "There, there," he said, "don't distress yourself. We'll get Big Bear Teddy Bear to make an announcement and ask if anybody has seen Teddy Bear Taylor tonight. It's just possible, you see, that he couldn't find a way out of his house. It does happen sometimes – one gets pushed right down to the bottom of the bedclothes and can't get out, or the bedroom door won't open or something of that sort. There's probably a perfectly reasonable explanation for it." And he went off to have a word with Big Bear Teddy Bear.

Big Bear Teddy Bear called attention and asked if anybody knew anything of the whereabouts of Teddy Bear Taylor. Nobody responded. Nobody had seen him. There was a great deal of shaking of heads and one teddy bear was heard to say that he'd heard of a case of a labrador dog waylaying a teddy bear on the way to the annual picnic one year and sleeping with him between his paws all night. The labrador dog has mistaken him for an old slipper he was very fond of – but all the same . . .

Little Teddy Bear gave a wail. "Oh do shut up!" he cried to the teddy bear who had related this awful incident.

"We must do something," said Big Bear Teddy Bear.

"Like what?" demanded a teddy bear with a torn ear.

"We must organize a search party," said Teddy Bear Smythe.

"What, and spoil our picnic all for the sake of one teddy bear?" said the one with the torn ear.

"We might never get back," said another.

"The food will spoil," said a third.

Big Bear Teddy Bear gave them a stern look. "How can you be so selfish," he said, "as to want to carry on as if nothing had happened when one of our brothers may be in trouble? Now I ask you once again – who will help to search for Teddy Bear Taylor?"

One by one the teddy bears raised their paws. Sad to say, some of them were rather reluctant to spoil the party, but their friends made them feel so ashamed that eventually they all set out with a better will. In groups of two or three they went along the path by which Teddy Bear Taylor must come to the picnic wood, searching every inch of the way for any clue to his whereabouts, but not a sign of him did they see. At length they all arrived at Teddy Bear Taylor's house. It was shut up and dark and there was no sound, but suddenly one of the bears said, "Hush, listen!"

A tiny moan came to them.

"Teddy Bear Taylor, is that you?" whispered Teddy Bear Johnson.

"Yes, it's me. I'm up here."

All the teddy bears looked up, and there was poor Teddy Bear Taylor huddled on the bathroom window sill, his front paws over his eyes.

"Can't you get down?" asked Teddy Bear Smythe.

"No."

"Can't you get back inside?" asked Teddy Bear Jones.

"No. The window slammed behind me."

"If we found a blanket and held it out for you, do you think you could jump into it?" asked Teddy Bear Johnson.

The only answer to that was an emphatic shake of the head.

"Then there's only one thing to be done," said Big Bear Teddy Bear. "We must get inside the house and wake up his owner."

The teddy bears looked at him in amazement. Only in the most dire emergency did teddy bears let their owners know that they could move and speak when they wanted to, but, as Big Bear Teddy Bear said, this was an emergency. Teddy Bear Taylor might fall at any moment. So they ran round to the back door, and they all pushed and pushed as hard as they could, until at last the door burst open and they were inside.

Up the stairs they went, only to find that the child's bedroom door was shut, but they soon solved that problem by Teddy Bear Johnson, Teddy Bear Smythe, and Teddy Bear Jones, the biggest of them all, standing on one another's shoulders so that Little Teddy Bear could climb up and turn the handle. They were inside the room.

They crowded round the bed. "It's a girl," said one teddy bear.

"I knew that," said Little Teddy Bear. "Her name is Susan."

"Do you think she will help?" asked Big Bear Teddy Bear.

"I'm sure she will," Little Teddy Bear replied. "Teddy Bear Taylor speaks very highly of her."

All the teddy bears climbed on to Susan's bed and began to shake her. It seemed to take a long time, but in reality it was only a minute or two before Susan sat up sleepily and looked at all the teddy bears. She did not speak.

"We need your help," said Big Bear Teddy Bear. "Your own teddy bear is stuck on the bathroom window sill and he can't get to the Teddy Bears' picnic. Can you go and let him in, please?"

Susan stared in bewilderment for a few minutes at her midnight visitors, but then she got out of bed and went to open the bathroom window. She reached out her hands and took her beloved teddy bear in her arms and cuddled him for a moment. Then she set him down on the floor. All his friends crowded round him and before long he was his usual cheerful self. "I'll have to think of a better way next year," he laughed, although he still looked pale. Then they all ran off to the picnic, and because of the adventure it was the best picnic they could ever remember. "There's something very satisfying about helping a friend," mused Teddy Bear Johnson as he lay back listening to the music.

"Yes," responded Teddy Bear Smythe, "I think we've all discovered that tonight."

In the morning, when Susan awoke, she saw that her teddy bear was lying so fast asleep at the bottom of the bed that she just covered him over with the quilt and left him. He had a very fat tummy.

"Mummy," she said when she went downstairs, "a strange thing happened last night."

Her mother listened to the story; then she smiled. "I used to have dreams like that myself," she said, "when I was a little girl."

* * *

Follow-up Discussion
This is a lovely story for the whole age range but it will probably have more impact with the younger children. Discussions about helping others should take place before and after the story. As the world of the very young is a very subjective place, emphasis should be placed on helping in the home and at school. The children will have very limited experience of other situations.

Language Development and Creative Writing
The children in this age group form quite close relatonships with their teddies and dolls. They could be encouraged to make up an adventure story about them. Depending on the ability of the children, this could be done either individually or in groups.

Environmental Studies and Science
The nightlife of a wood could be researched following this story. Most of the wildlife of woods and forests comes out at night.

The science involved in baking is quite considerable. A whole lesson could evolve around the cracking of an egg. The children could bake gingerbread bears.

Art and Craft
The picnic and all the ingredients that go into a picnic basket could be made from newspaper, card and the contents of the bits and pieces box.

Drama, Movement and Music
The older children could make a puppet theatre adaptation to be performed for the younger ones in the school. They could bring their own teddies to use as the puppets.

Many famous teddy bears have been made into cartoon stories. The children will be familiar with the Paddington Bear, Winnie the Pooh and Rupert Bear cartoons. They could be encouraged to imagine how a teddy bear moves and to demonstrate the movements.

"The Teddy Bears' Picnic", the classic children's song, is just one piece of music that can be used in connection with this story.

The Three Monsters

(Consideration for Others)

Once upon a time there was a knight called Sir Kenneth, who was neither very bold nor very brave, but everyone thought he was, because he rode a black horse and carried a big bronze sword. "There goes the brave Sir Kenneth," the people cried as he passed them, "off to fight a dragon, no doubt." And they would watch him as he rode off into the distance, thinking what a fine thing it must be to be so valiant.

The truth was, however, that Sir Kenneth had never fought a dragon in his life, nor ever wanted to, because he was at heart a quiet and gentle man, though rather pleased to be thought otherwise.

One day, hearing about Sir Kenneth's bravery, the people of a neighbouring land sent word that they had in their country three terrible monsters, of whom they would heartily like to be rid, for their roaring and stomping about all night kept them awake. They would be very much obliged, they said, if Sir Kenneth would go and fight the monsters for them.

When this news was brought to Sir Kenneth, he hardly knew what to do. He was too fond of his reputation as a valiant knight to admit that he didn't want to slay the monsters, so in the end he agreed to go. He hoped that something would happen before he got there, that would prevent his having to lift his sword against the creatures. When he arrived in the country where the monsters lived, he was greeted with jubilation. Wherever he went, the gentlemen bowed and the ladies curtseyed and all the children shouted "Hooray!"

Sir Kenneth was quite pleased. "Where are the monsters I have come to fight?" he cried, waving his sword, at the same time hoping that they had run away in fear and trembling at the mention of his name.

"There they are!" returned the people, pointing to the

mountains. "That is where they live, and for your convenience we have found you a nice dry cave where you can lie in wait for them."

Sir Kenneth was taken to the cave, and after looking around he said, "I might as well be comfortable whilst I am here. Bring me a table, a chair, and a bed."

"How brave he is!" the people exclaimed. "A table, a chair, and a bed for Sir Kenneth!"

When they had brought these things to him, the people retired to the city, leaving Sir Kenneth all alone, wondering what to do next. When night came, he heard a great roaring outside the cave, and when he looked out, there was the first of the three monsters. It was bright pink all over, with a long, fat tail, and simply *enormous* teeth, and it made Sir Kenneth shiver in his shoes. "Go away!" he cried. "I don't want to fight you. Go back to your mountain, there's a good chap."

The monster blinked at him, and, to Sir Kenneth's surprise, it started to wag its tail. "Will you pat me on the head?" said the monster. "All my life I have wanted someone to pat me on the head and be my friend, but when I ask them they always run away."

Sir Kenneth was very relieved. "Come in," he said. "I don't mind patting you on the head if that's all you want."

So the monster came in and sat down on the chair. Sir Kenneth patted him on the head and they chatted away like the best of friends.

The next night there was an even more terrible roaring outside the cave. Sir Kenneth was very frightened, but he knew that he would have to do something to stop the roaring, so he tiptoed outside. There stood the second monster; it was yellow and green, with red eyes and a huge whiskery chin, and it roared and it roared and it roared.

"What is the matter?" enquired Sir Kenneth. "Why do you roar at me like that? I don't want to hurt you. Please stop the noise. It frightens me."

The monster stopped roaring, and two great red tears rolled out of its great red eyes. "Will you chuck me under the chin?" he said. "I have a fancy for being chucked under the chin, but however much I roar, nobody will ever do it to me."

"If that's all you want," said Sir Kenneth, sighing with relief, "come into my cave. There's nobody here but my friend."

The monster came in and curled up on the table and Sir Kenneth chucked him under the chin and made him very happy.

On the third night there was the most horrible roaring of all, and this time Sir Kenneth was sure that the monster had come to gobble him up, but he peeped out all the same. There was a most dreadful green monster, with four eyes and seventeen legs, one of which was a wooden one, so that when he walked up and down in front of the cave he went *sixteen-bonk! sixteen-bonk! sixteen-bonk!* No wonder the people had been kept awake all night; no wonder they had been terrified of him. Sir Kenneth could hardly believe his eyes and his ears. "I must be dreaming this time," he thought. "There never could be a monster as ugly as that." But no sooner had the monster caught sight of him than it stopped stomping about and rolled over on its back with all its legs in the air.

Sir Kenneth ventured out and stood looking down at the monster. "What do you want?" he asked, and then stopped in amazement as he saw the expression on the creature's face. "Why!" he exclaimed. "I do believe you want me to tickle your tummy!"

"Yes please!" responded the monster, wriggling about on his back. "Oh do tickle my tummy! I love it more than anything!"

"You'd better come in," said Sir Kenneth. "I don't want anybody to see me tickling your tummy out here. I'm supposed to be a ferocious warrior."

When the monster went into the cave, he nodded to the other two monsters and settled himself down on the bed. Sir Kenneth tickled his tummy just as if he was an old, friendly dog, and soon all four of them were the best of friends.

When the people knew that the monsters had been tamed, they were so pleased that they built Sir Kenneth a new castle to live in, and he took the three monsters to live with him. After that, nobody asked him to fight any more monsters because, of course, they all thought he had done *quite* enough of that sort of thing!

* * *

Follow-up Discussion
Was Sir Kenneth brave or not? What does one have to do to be a brave person? Bravery is not just exhibited by shows of force. These points are worthy of discussion following this story.

There are many well-documented examples of people who have acted heroically, without using violent means. The children could be introduced to some of these, such as Grace Darling. In addition, the newspapers and television often feature stories at both national and local levels, of people who have shown bravery.

Language Development and Creative Writing
The older children could choose a heroic person and write a story in the first person. This could involve them in researching into that person's story.

The younger children could talk about the little things they like having done to them, such as being kissed before going to bed.

Environmental Studies
Research about knights, their training and good deeds is just one follow-up activity suggested by this story. It could be extended to include the conferring of knighthoods by the Queen in her honours list.

Art and Craft
The descriptions of the three monsters in the story lead into paintings of each of them. Similarly, models can be made from scrap materials and each monster could be given a name.

Drama, Movement and Music
Using monster masks, the children could act out this story in assembly.

The children could compose monster songs and music for monsters, based on Carl Orff methods.

The Terrible Scary Hairy Monster

(Consideration for Others)

Once upon a time, in a deep, dark cave beside the ocean, there lived a huge and terrible monster. He had eight great hairy legs with claws on the ends of them, which were so long that he could reach right down to the seashore, without any effort at all, to grab seaweed to eat, and pebbles, and driftwood, and anything else that came his way.

The children who lived in the nearby village had often been warned not to go near the cave, but of course some of them disobeyed the warning. They knew that the monster slept a great deal during the day, because he fed at night, and they thought it a splendid game to goad the monster and get as close as they could without being caught.

But one day one of them *was* caught.

The monster had been kept awake for many days by their shrieks and shouts, so he reached right out with one of his hairy claws and pulled the child into the cave. "A nice, plump, tasty morsel," he shouted, "but scarcely enough to make a meal. I will save him until I catch a few more, and have them for supper with salt and pepper."

When they heard what had happened, the child's parents were overcome with grief, for they thought they would never see their boy again. The other children were very frightened, and for a long time they kept well away from the cave, but as time went on they forgot their fear and began to say, "Let's go and tease the monster again!"

The sensible ones refused to go, but the others, without telling their parents what they intended to do, ran down to the seashore and crept towards the cave. The monster opened one eye, but kept quite still, so that the children would think he was sleeping. After a time, one of the children, a little girl, came close enough for him to reach out and grab her. She struggled and cried, but it was no use.

In a moment she had been thrust into the deepest part of the cave with the other child.

"Two plump, tasty morsels," roared the monster. "Shall I fry them, or roast them, or eat them raw with a nice bit of sea lettuce for garnishing?"

The childen ran away screaming, and it was a long time before they dared to tell anyone what had happened to their friend, but at last they had to admit that she had been captured by the terrible hairy scary monster.

And so it went on. For a short time after each child had been captured the others kept well away, but always the excitement of baiting the monster called them back, until no fewer than nine of the village children were missing.

"Give us back our children!" cried the parents. The monster only yawned and rolled over on his back and went to sleep again.

One day a new child named Cassie came to live in the village. She was curious as to why there were so few children there. When she was told the truth she said, "I will go down to the beach and see the monster."

"We'll come with you," the remaining children said, excitedly.

"No," said Cassie, "I want to go alone."

The children looked at her in disbelief. She was so small and thin that they were sure she wouldn't dare to go alone, so they simply ran away and left her.

But Cassie did go to see the monster.

"Wake up," she said as she approached the cave. "I want to talk to you."

Hearing a child's voice the monster said, "Come closer, my dear, come closer. I can't hear you very well."

Cassie went closer, and the monster, seeing her for the first time, roared with laughter. "You're not worth catching," he said. "Go away and send me a nice fat child instead."

"Don't be ridiculous," said Cassie. "I know you're not going to eat the children, so you might as well let them go."

The monster was so amazed at her confidence that he picked her up in one of his great hairy claws for a closer look. "You're a bold one," he said. "What makes you so sure that I won't eat you?"

"Because," said Cassie firmly, "I'm on your side."

"On my side!" he repeated.

"Yes," she said. "When I heard how shamefully the children had teased you I wasn't surprised that you'd caught them and put them where they couldn't bother you any more. I'd have done just the same if I had been in your place."

"Would you?" he gasped.

"Of course I should. Would you mind not holding me quite so tightly, please? I'm finding it rather hard to breathe."

"Sorry," said the monster, letting her go, and she sat down beside him, cross-legged, and gazed at him.

"I don't think you're so terrible," she said. "I think you're rather sweet."

The monster gulped back a tear. "That's the first kind word that anybody ever spoke to me," he said. "All my life people have said how horrid I was, and how ugly, and just because I was different from them the children taunted me and wouldn't let me sleep. I never bothered them at all until they started to do such things to me, but they didn't think how I felt." And he gave a sob that made the whole cave echo with the sound. "Even monsters want to be loved sometimes," he went on, "but no-o-o-o-body loves me!"

"Now stop feeling sorry for yourself," said Cassie, "and I'll see what can be done to put things right." And she gave him a kiss on the nose that made him blush and hide his face under his tail.

Cassie went down to the deepest part of the cave, where she found all the children weeping for fright at the noise the monster had made when he cried. When they saw Cassie they thought she, too, had been captured, and that made them more afraid than ever. "Now that he has ten children," they said, "he might think he has enough to make a good meal." They began to cry bitterly.

"For goodness sake stop that noise," said Cassie sternly.

The children were so surprised that they did stop.

"Come with me," she said, "and talk to the monster."

"Oh, no, no!" they cried, shrinking back.

"He won't hurt you," she told them. "Follow me."

Because she looked so confident, the children followed her, and when they got to the mouth of the cave, they saw the monster sitting there combing his hair.

"Now," said Cassie, "the first thing we must do is give him a name." She looked carefully at him. "How would you like to be called Chim-Chim?" she asked.

Chim-Chim blushed again and nodded several times. He had never had a name before.

"Now stroke Chim-Chim," she said to the children.

At first they were too afraid to touch him, but when they saw how he allowed Cassie to tickle him behind the ears, they approached him and began to stroke his hair.

Cassie said, "You must learn to live side by side with Chim-Chim and not call him a monster any more, just because he doesn't look like you. He can't help the way he looks. You must let him have his seaweed supper every night and his sleep during the day, and in return he will allow you to play on the beach. Surely the world is big enough to hold all of us!"

So the children agreed, and Chim-Chim allowed them to go home. Their parents were overjoyed to see them. After that they respected Chim-Chim's peaceful ways and the privacy of his home, and though they often played on the beach nearby, he never touched them. But once in a while, just to show there was no ill-feeling, he would allow them to go into the cave and comb his hair and polish his claws, and they would gather huge bunches of seaweed for his supper, which he gobbled up with the greatest enjoyment.

*   *   *

Follow-up Discussion
The discussion to follow this story can be about the ways in which we can show respect for others – by good manners, kindness and consideration, for example.

The other point worth discussing is that looks are often misleading. Beauty is only "skin-deep". In real life, sometimes, beautiful things can be dangerous. Water is a classic example. Conversely, many ugly things are harmless, only having their ugliness as a defence mechanism (e.g. frogs).

Language Development and Creative Writing
Descriptive discussion and writing about how the children imagine the scary hairy monster to look could result from this story.

Environmental Studies and Science
This story provides the teacher with possible environmental studies into either the seashore or caves. Both subjects have plenty of source material available.

Art and Craft
Paintings and models of the monster are the obvious creative activities to come from this story. Monster masks would be another possibility.

Drama and Movement

This story can be dramatized for use in assembly and the monster mask would be a useful prop.

Acting as if scared could be developed for a movement lesson. There are so many different reactions to indicate fear, depending on what is causing it. One would react differently if one was afraid of a noise in the dark than if one was afraid of a mouse or spider.

CHAPTER FOUR

Fantasy

The Good Fairies

(Caring and Sharing, Honesty, Tolerance, Cheerfulness in Adversity, Patience, Gentleness)

In the old days, when people believed in a great many things which are almost forgotten now, it used to be said that when a child was born, good fairies gathered around the cradle, bringing gifts of wisdom, truth, or other good fortune.

One day, there was born to a forester and his wife a dear little baby daughter. As the father gazed down at her, he said to his wife, "She is a very beautiful child."

His wife smiled. "Of course she is," she said. "I knew she would be, because the good fairy of beauty was at my bedside all night."

The forester said, "Surely, you don't believe in that old superstition! Our baby is beautiful because she is our child, that's all."

"But I do believe in it," protested the young mother. "I saw the good fairy quite plainly. She stood beside the cradle and touched our baby on the cheek and said she had brought her the gift of beauty."

The forester said no more, but went off to his work in the forest, leaving the mother and child alone in the house. The mother rocked her baby and sang to her. The child slept. Suddenly, the young mother heard a small commotion, and looking up, she saw another good fairy flying into the room. "I'm so sorry I'm late!" the fairy gasped, alighting on the bed-post and breathing rather fast, "but I'm afraid I lost my way. The forest is so dense and so enormous that I couldn't find your house."

The mother looked quite concerned. "I'm sorry you had so much trouble," she said gently. "Do sit down and rest before you say anything else. You must be quite exhausted."

The fairy sat down and looked steadily at the mother. "Aren't you curious to know what gift I have brought for your child?" she asked.

"Of course I am," smiled the mother, "but I can wait until you are recovered. Will you share a drink with me?"

The fairy drank tea with the mother, and when she had quite recovered her composure, she stood up and looked at the child. Touching her head, the fairy said, "I bring you the gift of patience." Then, without another look at the mother, she flew away.

A short time later there came a tapping at the window, which was just beside the bed where the young mother lay with her child at her breast. Thinking it might be a bird hungry for food, she opened the window to throw out some crumbs. As she did so, another fairy flew into the room. "Forgive me!" she gasped. "I know I'm very late, but I got caught in a butterfly net and couldn't get here in time to welcome your baby into the world."

"I do hope that you weren't harmed in any way," responded the young mother, anxiously. "Let me look at your wings. You haven't damaged them, have you?"

The good fairy replied, "No, but they are a little crumpled, so perhaps you would be kind enough to smooth them with your finger."

"Of course I will," the mother responded, and she stroked the good fairy's wings with her little finger until they were as smooth and beautiful as ever.

The fairy bent over the child and said, "I bring you the gift of gentleness." Then, with a smile, she vanished.

As the sun went down, the forester returned home to his wife and child. "Well," he enquired, "did you have any visitors today?"

"Oh yes!" his wife exclaimed. "First of all I had the good fairy of patience, who blessed our child with her gift, and then I had the good fairy of gentleness." She broke off and was silent for a few moments. Then she said, "You do believe me, don't you?"

The forester looked down at the sleeping child. "Yes," he said, "I do."

His young wife's face lit up. "I am glad," she said simply. "But what made you change your mind?"

He replied, "Well, as you know, the forest is very big, and nobody else can find their way through it as I can. On my way home I encountered several well-wishers looking for our house." He opened the door. "And here they are," he concluded.

And into the room came all the good fairies of the world,

bringing their gifts to the new-born child. Can you think what those good gifts were?

* * *

Follow-up Discussion
The last paragraph provides the opening for discussion. It is an open-ended story that invites the children to provide the ending. The discussion should proceed from this point. What qualities would the fairies bring to bestow upon the forester's daughter? The emphasis should be put on moral qualities rather than material things.

Language Development and Creative Writing
The children could be asked to imagine that they were the baby in the story. If they had their own choice of the qualities that the fairies could bestow upon them, what would they choose for themselves?

Environmental Studies and Science
The story is set in a forest and could provide the stimulus for a project on forestry. The Forestry Commission have a very comprehensive range of publications to assist in a topic of this nature. The range of study available in researching forestry can cover the whole curriculum.

Art and Craft
The art and craft activities suggested by trees or forestry are already an integral part of many school art and craft lessons. Other activities, such as relief impressions of leaves, twigs, and bark, are covered in the follow-up to "Isabella's Oak".

Drama
This story will adapt well for use as a play in assembly. It will give the girls an opportunity to perform fairy dances around the baby's cot. Many little girls harbour the dream of becoming ballet dancers and they enjoy pretending to dance like a ballerina.

Margery Moonlight and the Magic Party

(Consideration for Others, Kindness, Politeness, Teamwork)

Margery Moonlight, the good witch of Ringwater, went to watch the children playing on the village green. All the children knew that she was a witch, but they were not afraid of her. She had cured so many of them of the pox and the fever with her magic potions that they thought of her as their friend.

It was a beautiful day, the first of May. Margery Moonlight began to think that she would like to do something rather special for the children, who hadn't had a treat since Christmas Day. As she thought about what she might do with her magic powers she couldn't help noticing their behaviour towards each other. Some of the children were kind and pleasant, others were mischievous, but some were downright horrid, and that was a thing that Margery Moonlight couldn't bear to see. She began to make a plan.

"What are you thinking about, Margery Moonlight?" asked the children, crowding round her.

"A great many things," she replied. "I am thinking about springtime, and music, and good things to eat, and about children's parties."

The children asked what she meant, for it was in the days before parties had been thought of.

"I mean," she explained, "a gathering of all the children in one place to sing and dance, play games, and eat as much as they like, and have a special little gift to take home when they leave."

The children's eyes sparkled. Never had they heard of such things. How wonderful it sounded! "Will you do it for us, Margery Moonlight?" they begged. "Can you make us a magic party?"

"Oh yes," she said, without hesitation, "there's no difficulty about *that*. The only problem that I can see is whether you all deserve to come to my party."

"Of course we do!" the children cried.

"We shall see, we shall see," she smiled. "Come and sit on the edge of the green until the party is ready."

The children did as she bid them, but she noticed that some of the children took care to be at the front, so as to be first at the party, and one boy, whose name was Dandy, was so determined to have an advantage over the other children that he rudely pushed away anybody who came near him. Margery Moonlight noticed all this, but she said nothing.

Nor did she speak as she went about making the party. She didn't chant any magic rhymes or throw magic powder into a fire, or any mumbo-jumbo of that kind. All she did was sit with her chin on her hand looking intently at the village green.

In a very short space of time a group of musicians arrived. They grouped themselves together in one spot and began to play. Shortly afterwards a long table appeared in the centre of the village green, and before the children's astonished eyes the table spread itself with mouth-watering food. Festoons began to float in the air as if suspended from an unseen ceiling. Best of all, perhaps, was a huge box overflowing with toys.

"The trumpet is mine!" shouted Dandy. "Nobody else is to touch it. I'll knock down the first one who tries."

"Is the party ready yet?" asked one little girl. "Please may we go in?"

Margery Moonlight nodded her head. "If you can," she said.

The children rushed forward. They were very excited. They had never seen such good things to eat, never heard such music, never imagined such fine toys; but that was no excuse for the way they behaved. They pushed and jostled and fought in their attempts to get there first, and the worst one of all was Dandy.

Margery Moonlight blinked her eyes two or three times, and there must have been magic in it, because when the children came within an arm's length of the good things they found they could get no farther. It was as if they bumped into an invisible wall that kept them out. They fell down and rubbed their noses and chins where they had come up against the unseen barrier. Only one child walked through, and she was the girl who had asked permission to go in.

The other children tried over and over again to get inside, but it was no use. They groped their way all round the village green, feeling the wall with their fingers, but unable to find an entrance.

They stamped their feet. They threw such looks at Margery Moonlight as might have turned her to stone if she hadn't been a witch.

At length, two of the children ran over to her. "Please, Margery Moonlight," they said, "let us in." She smiled and nodded, and when the children tried once more to penetrate the barrier that had held them out, they found no difficulty in walking straight through. Gradually, it dawned on the children that they had been very ill-mannered. They felt ashamed. "Please, Margery Moonlight," they pleaded, "let us go in. We're sorry we've been so rude." And after that they found no trouble in getting to the party. The only boy left outside was Dandy. He was quite determined not to ask.

"Why don't you ask nicely if you can come in?" the other children called. "Why don't you say please?"

"I won't say please," Dandy cried. "I won't, I won't, I won't!"

The truth was, you see, that no-one had ever taught Dandy how to be polite, and he thought good manners were silly. He pretended that he didn't care, but the sight of the other children enjoying themselves so much made him angry. He pulled faces at them. He kicked at the barrier. He kept his eyes on the trumpet that he wanted so much.

At last he could bear it no longer. He went to Margery Moonlight, but he wouldn't look at her. He shuffled about on his feet, and kept his hands in his pockets, and stared at the ground. "I want to go in – please," he said.

"Well, Dandy," said Margery Moonlight, "you said it with bad grace, but at least you said it, so in you go."

Dandy didn't bother to say "thank you", but ran away immediately to the party. Oh, you should have seen him eat! He stuffed food into his mouth with both hands, so anxious was he to have as much as everybody else. Of course, like everything else at that party, the food was magic, and the more the children ate the more polite they grew. Dandy, who had begun by eating far more than was good for him, began to think that perhaps he was being rather impolite, and he drew back to allow the other children to take their share.

When it was time to play games, a great change had come over the children. They were courteous to each other. They laughed and enjoyed themselves, but it was all done with such good humour that Margery Moonlight saw that her plan had worked.

At the very end of the party the children took their leave of her. One by one they shook hands with the good witch of Ringwater and thanked her for a lovely party, after which they received one of the presents from the magic box. The surprising thing was that each one of them got the very present he or she had set their heart upon.

Last of all came Dandy. He thanked Margery Moonlight in the nicest possible way, and if there was the tiniest anxiety at the back of his mind that the trumpet might have already been given to somebody else, who can blame him? But to his delight it was still there, the only gift left at the bottom of the box. Margery Moonlight handed it to him with a smile. He put it to his lips and blew, and at the first sound from the magic trumpet everything on the village green disappeared. Only Dandy was left standing there, the trumpet in his hand and a pleasanter feeling in his heart than he had ever felt before.

Margery Moonlight was never seen in the village again. Nobody knew where she had gone. But the children never forgot her. They grew up into courteous, considerate men and women, and Dandy was the pride of them all.

*   *   *

Follow-up Discussion
This is another story that can be used when the children are going through a phase where the common niceties are being omitted.

The discussion points that can be developed from the story include the basic good manners of "please", "thank you" and "excuse me" – all very short phrases that are neither painful nor costly.

This can be extended to include the ways in which the children should conduct themselves at parties – being able to play together without fighting and squabbling; being a good loser in party games; knowing when to say "No" to that extra piece of cake; knowing the correct way to accept presents.

Language Development and Creative Writing
Within the classroom the children could be asked to plan their own perfect party. Who would they invite if their choice was limitless? What games would they choose to include? If they had their way, what would they have to eat?

The older children could learn how to write a letter inviting a friend to a party and how to write back, accepting the invitation.

Environmental Studies and Science

Some of the edibles which children enjoy at parties could be prepared quite simply, even by the youngest children. This would involve the children in a variety of scientific and mathematical activities.

Art and Craft

The older children could design a birthday or Christmas cake decoration.
The younger children could make crackers and simple party hats.

Drama, Movement and Music

The story is ideal for use as a play in assembly. It provides an excellent opportunity for the classic mime situation "trying to find a way through a sheet of glass or invisible barrier".

Many children's party games can be used in movement lessons, such as "Statues". The children could mime eating in different ways – daintily, greedily, hungrily, or when they do not like what they are eating.

The choice of music for this story is very broad and varied.

Food From The Forest

(Caring and Sharing, Honesty)

A long time ago, before the days of the motor car and the aeroplane, there was a little village standing all alone in the heart of a great country. The people of the village were poor; they depended for their food upon their own harvests; but they were happy because they all helped one another and lived like one big family.

It happened one year that after a cold spring and a cloudy summer, the harvest failed. There was little corn for grinding into flour to make bread, and the people knew that they must face a harsh and hungry winter. However, they made the best of things by storing up whatever they could for the months ahead, each family contributing whatever they could to the general store. One man had been successful in growing some fine turnips; a woman who took great pride in her apple tree and her hive of bees gave fruit and honey. Those who had chickens agreed that they would share their eggs. It was little enough, but what there was would be for the good of all.

The days went by. The nights grew colder. Because they were hungry the children cried, and the old people shivered with cold. The oldest inhabitant of the village was a man named Vashky. He was so old that even his two children had died of old age, but Vashky himself was as hale and hearty as it was possible for such an old man to be. He had always taken good care of himself.

One afternoon Vashky took his hand-cart into the nearby forest to collect firewood, but as most of the fallen timber had already been collected and distributed to those who needed it most, Vashky found that he had to wander farther and farther into the heart of the forest in order to find it. Although he had lived there all his life and thought he knew the forest as well as he knew his own face, he soon found himself walking along a path he had never trodden before. So narrow and overgrown was this path that he had to leave his cart in a small clearing and proceed without it. He was quite mystified. As a boy he had played hide and seek in this very spot, but he had never seen this path before.

He found several fallen branches, which he gathered up and took back to his cart, then once more set off along the mysterious pathway to see what else he could find. As he went on he was surprised to hear voices. Villagers, perhaps, felling a tree? But no – the woodman wouldn't allow that. Only fallen timber was allowed to be taken away. Then who could these people be who were talking and laughing and singing snatches of songs as they worked? He stepped forward more cautiously. Still he could see nobody. Suddenly a most delicious smell of cooking came to his nose. Somebody was cooking a meal in the very heart of the forest. Who could it be?

Truth to tell, Vashky was rather frightened. He thought he had stumbled upon a robbers' den, and was just about to creep away before the strangers spotted him, when something white attracted his attention. The voices had ceased completely. Not a sound broke the silence of the forest. What was it that stood so still and silent beyond the brambles? He crept forward, still attracted by the delicious smell.

A moment later a most astonishing sight presented itself to him. There, in a clearing, was a table spread with a pure white cloth, and upon it the most wonderful dishes that Vashky had ever seen. A great bowl of steaming soup stood in the centre of the table, surrounded by pies and cakes and fruit and nuts in quantities undreamed of by anyone as poor as Vashky.

For a few moments all he could do was stare open-mouthed at the feast spread out before him. Then his eyes began to wander fearfully around the clearing. Not a soul was in sight, no hint of any habitation; nothing stirred but the steam from the soup. Vashky approached the table. It was too much, he argued with himself, to expect a man as hungry as himself to look at such food without tasting. Surely nobody would be so cruel as to expect him to creep away without at least a spoonful of soup.

He leaned forward. To his surprise, his eye caught sight of a small rectangular card resting against the soup tureen, with his name written upon it! Very cautiously, almost as if he thought it might bite, Vashky picked it up. The thought came to him that perhaps, after all, some kind soul had heard of his hunger and had prepared this meal especially for him. He turned over the card and was even more surprised to see that it bore a rhyme. This is what it said:

Choose whate'er you fancy best,
Eat your fill and share the rest.

Well, you may be sure that Vashky lost no more time in obeying the instructions on the card. He had soup, and a huge pie, and several cakes, two apples, and a handful of nuts. Without doubt, it was the best meal that Vashky had ever eaten, and through it all not a soul appeared to challenge his right to it.

When he could eat no more, he picked up the card again and studied the words more carefully. "Share the rest," he murmured to himself. "That can mean only one thing – I am to share my feast with my friends in the village, for there is nobody else I can share it with." Seizing a hamper that lay nearby, he filled it with the remains of the feast, and with a final glance at the table, hurried off to the place where he had left his cart. He placed the hamper behind the firewood and began the journey back to the village. By now it was getting quite dark, and although he made his way home as fast as he could, he was too replete to reach the village before everybody had gone to bed.

All the way home he had been thinking with great joy of the good news he was bringing to his friends. The children would be delighted with the biscuits, the sick would welcome the fruit, mothers who had starved themselves to feed their families would be thankful for the bread. But as he came abreast of his own house, Vashky's thoughts began to take a different turn. "I am old," he told himself, "the oldest man in the village. All my life I have worked hard for poor rewards. Surely the time has come when I deserve a little extra comfort? Who knows, this may be my last winter on earth? Would it be so wrong of me to make it the best? Better times may come for the young folks. I will put away this hamper of food for myself, and tomorrow I will go into the forest again. If the table should be there again, and full of food, I will bring it back for my friends."

In the darkness he unloaded the hamper and hid it beneath his bed. He left the firewood where it was until the morning. Conscience kept him awake for a great part of the night, and in the morning the same reason kept him away from the other villagers. He could not meet the hungry eyes of the children, the anxiety of parents. He ate a little of the bread for breakfast, and in the afternoon he set off once more with his cart.

He had no difficulty in finding the clearing, and to his delight saw the table set as before, with the same card bearing his name, the same rhyme written on the back. Once more he ate all he could, and once more he filled a hamper with the rest. He was hardly aware of his action, but he was careful to heap firewood over the hamper so that it could not be seen by anyone passing him on the way home. And when he arrived back in the dark it was easier than it had been the previous night to stow the hamper underneath his bed, telling himself that in the morning he would carry it into the village. He slept more easily that night, too, and breakfasted well in the morning. "I won't take the hamper just yet," he told himself. "Perhaps a little later, for they seem to be managing quite well without it just now."

He had a nap during the morning, and when he awoke he thought it was much too late for him to go into the village, for he had to make his trip into the forest again. And so the hamper remained where it was, with the other. That night Vashky brought home a third, and the following night a fourth. And so it went on. His hoard grew until there was no more space left underneath his bed and he had to conceal the hampers in the woodshed, but still he could not bring himself to share the food with the other villagers. Having been short of food all his life he was afraid that what he had now might in some mysterious way disappear. He was afraid to tell his friends how he had come by it, afraid that when they heard his story they might follow him to the secret place in the forest and spoil everything. So he watched the children growing thinner, the old people weaker.

One day, after having feasted as usual and started on his homeward journey with the hamper in his cart, he thought he heard stealthy footsteps behind him. "Who's there?" he cried, and stopped, and looked around, but there was nobody in sight. "It's my imagination," he told himself. Still he could hear the footsteps. Time and again he looked back to see who it was, but it was too dark to detect anyone.

He slept uneasily that night. The following afternoon he took his usual walk. Somehow his legs were heavy and his conscience pricked him as it had never pricked him before. He reached the clearing, but stopped in dismay when he beheld – nothing! No table, no food, no delicious smells. His heart began to pound uncomfortably. He felt that he was being watched. "Who's there?" he demanded. "Come out and show yourselves!" But nobody came, and he was afraid. He was just turning to run away when he saw the card lying at his feet. Picking it up he read these words:

Nevermore shall forest fare
Be spread for one who will not share.

Upon reading these words, Vashky was overcome with shame and remorse. He was also more afraid than he had ever been. He ran as fast as his old legs would carry him. He would go straight home and share his booty with his friends, no matter what time it was. He would rouse them from their beds. He would tell them the whole truth.

Fighting for breath the old man reached his house. He went straight to the store in the woodshed. One glance told him that the hampers had gone. He ran into the house to look underneath his bed. Not a crumb remained. He sank down on his knees, his eyes full of tears.

Suddenly there came a frantic knocking at the door. Vashky sprang to his feet in horror. He had a confused idea that the mysterious people who had spread the feasts for him had come to seek vengeance on him for his selfishness. The knocking continued, and then a voice said, "Are you there, Vashky? Do come out. A wonderful thing has happened, and I have been sent to fetch you. Come quickly!"

Vashky opened the door to find one of the village boys dancing on the doorstep from sheer delight. "What is it?" asked Vashky. "What has happened?"

"A gift!" cried the boy. "A wonderful gift. Hampers of delicious food left on the green, by whom nobody knows. There's enough to see the winter through for all of us! Oh, Vashky, come and get your share!"

Slowly Vashky made his way to the appointed place. All the villagers were gathered there. The older children had been given the delightful task of sharing out the food. Vashky hung back. He could not bring himself to take a portion of what he had been so unwilling to share.

"Come, Vashky!" the villagers cried. "You must take your share. It is very good of you to deprive yourself, but there is more than enough for all."

Vashky stepped forward and held up his hand. He spoke. He

confessed everything, how he had discovered the secret place, how he had intended to share the bounty but had been unable to do it, right up to the moment when he had come back home to find it gone. During the telling of the sorry tale he had kept his eyes on the ground, afraid to look in the faces of his friends, but when he looked up, he saw that they were not angry with him, but sympathetic. "Poor Vashky," said one. "I think I might have been tempted like him if I had found such bounty for the taking. Most of us don't know what it is like to be so old, so cold, but we have all been tempted to do wrong at times." He looked at the other villagers. "What do you say?" he shouted. "Shall we forgive him?"

"Yes!" was the cry.

So they took Vashky's hands and led him back home. There they had a magnificent feast, and nobody ever mentioned Vashky's temptation again.

*   *   *

Follow-up Discussion

A discussion on the question of sharing would be the natural progression from this story. It could be developed to include organizations which help people who are under-nourished and poorly clothed, such as the Red Cross, Oxfam and Help the Aged. How do these organizations operate? Where do they go to help and how do they raise their funds?

The children could also discuss the story's ending. The villagers forgave Vashky for succumbing to his temptations. The power to forgive people when they have done something wrong is a most important lesson for life.

Language Development and Creative Writing

Some very young children who are in their first year in school are probably experiencing the sharing of playthings with other children for the very first time in their lives. They could be encouraged to talk about this experience.

Sharing could also form part of the follow-up for the older children, because from time to time they need to be reminded that it is wrong to be selfish. This story lends itself to use at times when there is an outbreak of squabbling over the things in school.

Environmental Studies and Science

The organization of the village suggests a research project into the feudal agricultural system of the pre-industrial age, strip farming, and cooperatives.

Another project could be based on the title of the story. What food can be derived from the forest? This could develop into an ecological study of a forest.

The children could look at different aspects of food storage. This could include the ways in which plants and animals store food for the winter. Freezing is only one way by which we store and preserve food. Can the children discover other ways that we use nowadays? How did people store food for the winter before the introduction of refrigeration?

Art and Craft
The children could make a model of a medieval village with the fields surrounding it. They could plan the types of crops that would be growing in the fields and the animals that would be kept by the villagers. The village of Laxton in Nottinghamshire still operates on the medieval lines and could be used as a starting point.

Drama and Movement
This story will adapt well for use as a play in assembly.

Tilling the land could be a theme for a movement lesson. Walking behind a horse-drawn plough, scattering the seeds, hoeing the rows of growing crops and harvesting will provide some good material for movement and mime.

The Old Woman of The Woods

(Consideration for Others, The Importance of Friendships)

The old woman of the woods lived long ago, in the days when magic was commonplace and many strange things happened which could never be explained. She was so old that even the oldest inhabitants of the nearby village could not remember a time when she was young. As far back as they could recall she had been an old woman living in her wooden hut with only her animals for company, for the old woman of the woods was not only old, but very, very ugly, and who wanted to keep company with such an ugly creature as she?

She lived on milk from her goat, on eggs from her chickens, and on the nuts and fruit she gathered from the trees. For her clothing and her blankets she took wool from her sheep. She gathered thistledown to make pillows for her bed. She drank water from the woodland well. She had everything she needed except the company of another human being.

It was the delight of the village children to go into the woods and taunt the old woman.

"Mary, Mary Miseryskin,
Warts on her nose
And a cleft in her chin,"

they used to chant, dancing round the trees. The old woman was so glad to see the children that she didn't mind what they cried. When she heard them coming she used to run out to greet them, but they only thought she was coming out to harm them, for of course everybody said that she must be a witch. Then the children would run away, shrieking, half afraid and half excited at the cruel game that they were playing, and the old woman would go back indoors and feel very sad.

Now among the children of the village there was one little girl who never joined in the games of the others. Her name was Kirsty, and she was lame. She could not run away like the other children and so she never went into the woods with them, but even if she had not been lame she wouldn't have gone there to taunt the old woman, for Kirsty was kind.

One day she was gathering blackberries from the hedges on the edge of the wood when she saw a black and white goat entangled in the briars. She knew at once that it was the goat belonging to the old woman of the woods. Without hesitation she went forward to free the animal, and soon it jumped out of the briars and stood there looking round.

"Go home, Nanny Goat," laughed Kirsty. "Your mistress will be wondering what has become of you."

The goat didn't move.

"What's the matter?" said Kirsty. "Don't you know your way home?"

Still the goat stood there.

"Well, I can see I shall have to take you home," said Kirsty, "for your mistress will be wanting your milk before long."

She set off along the woodland path. She had to go slowly because of her weak leg, and the goat followed her. It was some time before they arrived at the old woman's hut, but she was delighted to see her goat again. "Aren't you afraid of me, child?" she said to Kirsty. "You know they say I am a witch."

"Oh no," said Kirsty, "I don't believe that." She smiled at the old woman and didn't seem to notice her ugliness. "May I come in and rest for a while?" she asked. "I am very tired."

The old woman took her in and gave her food and drink. She bathed the child's feet in pure well water, and all Kirsty noticed of the old woman was that her voice was gentle and that her hands were firm and good.

After that Kirsty went to visit the old woman once every week, and each time she went her leg seemed to grow a little stronger, for the exercise was good for it.

As for the old woman, she looked forward eagerly to the child's visits. A smile began to brighten up the face that had always worn a frown of unhappiness. For Kirsty's sake she used to wash and brush her hair until its silvery-whiteness began to shine again. She put sweet-smelling oil on her face and in time the warts began to disappear, and the cleft in her chin showed only as a dimple when she laughed.

Of course, those were the days when people believed in magic, and everyone said that the child must have enchanted the old woman, but anyone can make that kind of magic by using a little kindness. Can't they?

*   *   *

Follow-up Discussion
"Beauty is in the eye of the beholder" is a saying that is in common use. This story helps to emphasize the point.

Kirsty was prepared to practise this with the old woman. They strike up a relationship from which both of them derive pleasure and benefit. The gap between the child's generation and that of the grandparents is often quite small. This story can be used to illustrate that both generations have something to offer each other.

The children can discuss ways in which children can show kindness to the older generation

Language Development and Creative Writing
The question "What is beautiful?" can be discussed. Everybody has different ideas about what they like or dislike. To restrict this to the visual will probably reveal the predictable. If the likes and dislikes of smell, taste, touch and hearing are explored, more surprising responses may ensue. I did this with my children and we were talking about the sounds we liked and disliked and one child said that she hated the sound of chips frying. This prompted some very valuable discussion.

Environmental Studies and Science
The old woman lived a life of self-sufficiency in the woods. The children could research this by trying to find out just what the wood could or could not provide.

Art and Craft
Some of the creative activities provided by woods and trees have been dealt with in the follow-up suggestions to other stories, like "Isabella's Oak".

The old lady took wool from the sheep to make blankets. Making blankets suggests weaving and there are many attractive forms of weaving that require only a simple weaving frame or loom and inexpensive material. Odd balls of wool collected from home can be blended to get the best colour contrasts. Drinking straws and strips of card can be interlaced.

Those schools which have access to scraps of sheep's wool collected from the country could develop a project on cleaning and dyeing. The dyes could also be made from the juice of fruits and other natural compounds. This project opens up a scientific topic which can be developed over a long period.

Drama and Movement

This story will adapt well as a play for use in assembly. The old lady can be made up with face paints. We have used this play in assembly and the children enjoyed taunting the old lady and being "afraid of her". The girl who took the part of the old woman and was made up as suggested became a very convincing witch-like character.

A Long-Ago Story of the Mountain Pixies

(Helpfulness, Kindness, Resisting Temptation, Teamwork)

Nobody knows when the Diminy Pixies first went to live in the Dolorous Mountains, but one thing is certain – they were there one hundred years ago, because this story concerns something that happened then.

I must first of all tell you that in that part of the world there are two kinds of pixie. There is the Diminy Pixie, who is a shy, good little creature, moving about only by night, and doing what good he can whilst people sleep; and the Bragfoot Pixie, who is a very different character indeed, who loves to make people do evil things and to put all sorts of mischief into their heads. He, too, works whilst people sleep.

Late one night, over a hundred years ago, a shepherd named Fergus was returning to his hut at the foot of the mountains after tending a sick lamb, when he heard first a tiny squeal of alarm and then a splash as of something no bigger than a stone falling into the stream. It was a dark night, but Fergus was used to that and his eyes were keen. "Who's there?" he cried, peering into the water. "Tell me where you are and I'll help you."

"Here, here!" came a little voice, and hurrying in the direction from which the sound was coming, Fergus saw a tiny fellow clinging to a rock in the middle of the stream. He was only the size of a man's hand, and the rock to which he was clinging was merely a stepping stone. The running of the shallow stream must have seemed to him like a raging torrent, however, for it was evident that he was very frightened indeed. He cried once more for help, and Fergus was able, without any difficulty, to pick him up and lift him to safety on the edge of the wooden footbridge.

Fergus knelt down by his side and looked into his wide brown eyes. "Well!" he said. "All my life I've said I didn't believe in fairies and goblins and now here I am rescuing one with my very own hands from the stream. What are you, exactly, if I may ask?"

"I'm a Diminy Pixie," said the little chap, "and I must thank you for saving my life."

"You're welcome, I'm sure," said Fergus in his good-natured way. "Goodnight to you, and pleasant dreams."

"Stay a moment longer," pleaded the Diminy Pixie. "Can you direct me to the top of the mountain? I seem to have lost my way."

"You want to go to the top of the mountain?" said Fergus in astonishment. "Why, bless you, on those little legs of yours it will take you a week to get up there."

The Diminy Pixie began to look really alarmed. "Do you mean that I couldn't get back before daylight?" he cried. "Not even if I ran all the way?"

"That's about it," replied Fergus. "I reckon that the sun will be up long before you could reach the top of the mountain."

"Oh my eyes!" exclaimed the little fellow. "I can't stay out in the daylight. My eyes would never be able to stand the glare. Oh dear, what shall I do?" And he put his head in his hands and began to shiver.

Fergus pulled out of his shepherd's purse the swaddling cloth which he used for his new-born lambs, "You'd better get out of those wet clothes," he said, "and put this on. We'll talk about getting you up the mountain when you're warm and dry."

He politely turned his back whilst the Diminy Pixie took off his wet clothes and made a kind of garment from the swaddling cloth. Then he turned and asked the pixie how he came to be lost.

"I was out looking for moss," replied the pixie. "I'm a pillow pixie, you see – that means I make pillows for all the rest of my family. We Diminy Pixies are all one big family and we need a lot of pillows. I'm not very clever, so I don't go out on missions of kindness like some of my brothers, but I enjoy my work because it's so important for everybody to have a comfortable pillow, isn't it?" Fergus nodded, and the Diminy Pixie continued, "Well, I saw the most beautiful piece of sheep's wool blowing in a thorn bush that was overhanging a ravine, and though I knew it was dangerous to try to get it, I did, and I fell, and then I didn't know where I was, and I fell again, and I slithered, and – oh, I don't know what I didn't do before I fell into the water!"

"Well, it's all over now," said Fergus, "so there's no need to worry any more. I'll carry you back up the mountain, for I know it as well as I know the back of my hand, and we shall soon be there. Climb on to my hand and I'll put you in my shepherd's purse – there, you see? – isn't that cosy?''

The little fellow settled down quite comfortably and in no time at all was fast asleep, exhausted with all his adventures. Fergus began the ascent of the mountain. The Dolorous Mountains are very high, and the mountain which Fergus was ascending was the highest one of all. It took a long time for him to reach the summit, but when he did he gently shook his little friend awake and told him where they were.

The Diminy Pixie poked his head out and sniffed the air like a fox. "I'm home!" he cried. "I'm home, and it's still dark! Oh, how can I thank you, my good friend?"

"Think nothing of it," said Fergus. "Goodnight to you and be more careful when you are out at night." He set him down on the ground and turned and strode away. He was far too polite to watch and see where the Diminy Pixie went, for that was no business of his, and in any case Fergus was feeling tired and ready for his own bed.

He had descended only a little way when a small stone in his shoe made him stop to remove it. As he laced up his shoe again, he thought he heard the murmur of pixie voices coming from somewhere lower down on the mountain path. Thinking that they must be Diminy Pixies coming home from the missions of kindness which his little friend had mentioned, Fergus decided to conceal himself behind a rock and not seem to be spying on them. A moment later the pixies were close enough for him to hear what they were saying. There seemed to be only two of them.

"This is the way he came – oh yes, this is the way," said one.

"And it isn't very far to the top now," responded the other, with a chuckle in which Fergus was surprised to hear a hint of mischief. "We shall soon find them out, and then what fun we'll have!"

"Oh yes," returned the first one, "what fun, what fun!"

The chuckles that followed these speeches were so full of wickedness that Fergus knew these could not be the brothers of the Diminy Pixie whom he had helped. He cautiously peeped out. To his dismay he saw that whilst the two little men were about the same size and were dressed in much the same way as the Diminy Pixie, their faces were quite different. Craftiness and cunning were written in every line. He knew at once that their presence on the mountain boded no good to the Diminys, so he decided to follow them.

When they reached the spot where Fergus had set down the Diminy Pixie they paused and looked all around them. They cupped their ears in their hands and listened intently. Suddenly, one of the two, who seemed to be the elder, darted forward towards two huge rocks, and there he fell down on his knees and gestured to his companion to come and look. Fergus saw that they were peering into the gap between the two rocks. They had found the home of the Diminy Pixies!

Fergus was just about to step forward and snatch up the two intruders when they slipped into the crack and disappeared. Rushing over there, Fergus applied his eye to the gap. He was looking into a cavern lit only by a curious blue light, like the light of stars. The cavern was full of little men, little women, and tiny children, all Diminy Pixies. They were gathered round the little fellow whom Fergus had assisted and they were listening to the story of his night's adventure. Some of them seemed to be gently teasing him about the strange garment he was wearing. His own wet clothes were drying before a fire.

The two bad pixies were creeping down a winding staircase on the wall of the cave and as yet had not been noticed by the Diminys beneath, but even as Fergus watched, one of them suddenly raised his head as if he had sensed the presence of strangers. "Bragfoots!" he cried, shrinking away in evident terror. All the others followed him, crouching against the farthest wall, trembling and moaning with fear. Fergus was greatly puzzled. The Diminys outnumbered the Bragfoots by thirty to one. Why did they not rush upon them and turn them out? Why did they not attack? Why were they so afraid?

"Diminy Pixies," called out the elder Bragfoot in a soft and sinister voice, "we have found out your new hiding place. We have come to take you with us. Learn our ways, run away with us to the Bragfoot Camp and find how pleasant it is to be wicked instead of good."

"So easy," put in the other Bragfoot, "so very ea-ea-easy." And they both laughed with a very unpleasant sound.

The poor Diminys put their hands over their ears as if to shut out the voices, but the Bragfoots only raised them higher and continued to call to the Diminys to join them. Fergus could bear it no longer. He put his mouth to the aperture and called out, "Diminy Pixie, here I am – I, Fergus, who helped you home tonight. Do you need my help? Tell me what I can do."

There was a long silence. Even the Bragfoot Pixies seemed stricken dumb by the sound of the voice that echoed around the cavern like the voice of a roaring wind. At last, into the silence came a small, shaky voice. "Fergus? Is it really you?"

"Aye," replied the shepherd. "Tell me what I can do."

The Bragfoots put their heads together and began to whisper to each other, their pale eyes glinting like steel as they directed them towards the gap where they knew that Fergus must be. The Diminys, talking in frank and open voices, began to ask their little brother if the voice really did belong to a friend. Was he to be trusted? Could he keep a secret? Was he kind?

From their conversation, Fergus learnt that the little man whom he had helped was named Quill, and it was Quill who at last took courage to speak to Fergus on behalf of his huge family. "Diminy Pixies," he said, whilst the Bragfoots sneered, "do not fight. We have no means of defending ourselves against them. They are bad pixies and they say they will never rest until they have taught us to be like them. We try to hide from them, we don't want to listen to them, but when they find us out they are so persuasive that sometimes they tempt one of us to join them and go into evil ways. Take them away from here, Fergus, take them away so that they never come back."

"You must help me," responded Fergus.

"How?" asked Quill.

"By showing them that good is stronger than bad. Let the Bragfoots have their say. Listen to them. And when they have done, let them see that not one of you is tempted. That is the only way to force them out. They are beyond *my* reach."

Hearing all this, and confident that they would win, the Bragfoots began to bombard the poor little Diminys with words. They told them how exciting it was to do bad deeds, what fun there was in wrecking things, that it was silly to do good, and all the while Fergus watched their faces. He saw how ugly they became as they remembered past misdeeds, and how horribly their teeth showed in their evil smiles.

The Diminys at first shrank away from them. One or two of the younger ones took a step or two towards the Bragfoots, then stopped and drew back again. But when the Bragfoots paused, the Diminys turned and faced them, and amazingly the bad pixies retreated a step. Taking courage, the Diminys edged even further forward, and again the Bragfoots had to retreat. Fergus remained silent. It was not for him to encourage them now. Again, but this time with less conviction, the Bragfoots began their taunts, but they were getting weaker as the Diminys got stronger. The battle continued for some time, until at last there was nowhere else for the Bragfoots to go but out through the crack. Angry, flushed, and hideously ugly, the Bragfoots rushed out of the cavern – straight into the shepherd's purse which Fergus had placed in their way.

Quick as a flash he fastened the straps and hoisted the purse on to his shoulder. Oh how he laughed as he felt them struggling and fighting each other inside, how deaf to their persuasive voices! By mountain tracks unknown to anyone but the shepherd and his flocks he carried them, up and down, in and out, across ravines and streams and gullies, until nobody but himself could have retraced the way he had come.

At last he came to a dark, entangled wood, and there he stopped, put down the purse, and released his victims. They jumped up and down in their rage, shaking their fists and yelling at him. They kicked his shoes but only hurt their own toes. They tried to follow him as he strode out of the wood, but he left them far behind and soon he was so far away that even their shouts had ceased to reach his ears.

He was very tired. He paused once, and once only, to look up at the mountain where the Diminy Pixies lived. Then, with a light heart, he went home to bed. He knew that it would take a long, long time for the Bragfoots to find their way out of the wood, and longer still for them to climb up to the top of the mountain, by which time, he thought, if they had any sense at all, the Diminys would have blocked up the entrance to their cave and found some other means of entry.

But of course, he thought, just before he fell asleep, they could always leave it as it was – just as long as they remembered how to deal with their wicked little enemies.

*   *   *

Follow-up Discussion

This story should be told or acted out in two parts. In this way, the moral implications for each episode can be dealt with separately.

The first act is obviously devoted to helpfulness, kindness and giving a service without expecting a reward. This final point is probably the most important one. Today, far too many people expect a reward for the most insignificant of actions.

In the discussion that follows the second act, the children may need some guidance in understanding the implications of temptation. Many of them will have already discovered that there are occasions when it is easier to do the wrong thing than the right, and that it is necessary to face up to and resist people who tempt them into an improper action.

Language Development and Creative Writing

Those children who are not involved in either reading or acting the play could be asked, at the end of part one, to discuss and write about how they imagine the story will conclude.

Environmental Studies and Science

The story takes place at night and it could stimulate a study of nocturnal animals. Why do most animals come out during the night rather than during the day?

Art and Craft

The Diminy Pixies and their cave would make a wonderful frieze. The children could paint the expressions on the faces of the good and bad pixies.

Drama

This will make a very good two-act play for which the children will dress up. Face paints could be used to accentuate the expressions of good and evil of the Diminy and Bragfoot Pixies.

The Wish That Came True

(Tolerance, Cheerfulness in Adversity)

Mr Jasper was a very lucky man. He had everything he needed. He had plenty of money. He had a nice house. He had a car that never broke down. And he had a wife who was cheerful and contented.

But Mr Jasper wasn't cheerful – oh, no! – nor was he contented. You see, Mr Jasper kept wishing that he was young again. "Because," he said to Mrs Jasper, "if I were young again I could work harder and earn even more money than I do now, and think of all the lovely things I could buy. Besides," he added wistfully, "if I were younger, I shouldn't be so fat, and I shouldn't have a bald spot on the top of my head, and I'd be able to run about like I used to. I *wish* I could grow younger every day, instead of older."

Mrs Jasper, who was sensible as well as cheerful and contented, said, "You ought not to make wishes of that sort. Wishes are like sneezes – once they're out, you can't get them back in again, and you never know the consequences of either wishes or sneezes."

Mr Jasper didn't listen to her. He kept on wishing and wishing, until one night when the moon was green and the wind was blowing down the chimney and there was a lot of magic about, he wished too hard. When he awoke in the morning he felt different. "I feel younger," he said, jumping out of bed, and rushed to a mirror to look at himself. A big smile spread itself all over his face. "I *am* younger!" he cried, as Mrs Jasper came running in to see what all the fuss was about. Sure enough, there was a little hair beginning to grow on the bald patch on the top of his head, and he was certainly slimmer. He ran downstairs, singing as he went, and tucked into the biggest breakfast he had eaten for many a long year.

"Aren't you pleased that I wished so hard?" he asked his wife.

She replied cautiously, "I'm certainly glad that you feel so well, but as to the rest, I think it would have been better if you had left well enough alone. Remember what I said about wishes and sneezes."

"Oh, that doesn't signify anything," retorted Mr Jasper scornfully.

Every day after that, Mr Jasper grew a little younger, just as he had wished to do. His hair became quite dark again, and grew over the bald patch on the top of his head; his shoulders became straighter, and he found that he could run upstairs two at a time. He was perfectly satisfied with the way his wish had come true and went off to work every morning with a countenance as cheerful as anybody could wish.

Mr Jasper worked in an office, where he did sums every day in a big red book. The people who worked in the office began to notice that he was looking younger. "How do you do it?" they enquired.

"I just wished," laughed Mr Jasper, "and my wish came true."

All his friends began to wish as hard as they could, to see if it would work for them, but nothing came of their wishes. As anybody will tell you who knows about magic, the moon has to be green when the wind is blowing down the chimney before anything of the sort can happen, and even then you might just as easily get a cold in the head.

Everything went well until, one day, Mr Jasper noticed that he couldn't quite reach up to his books when he sat at his desk in the office, and somehow his sums seemed to be getting more difficult, and all his friends appeared to him to be very old. One day later, as Mr Jasper was getting dressed in the morning, he found that his trousers were too long. He didn't know what to do. Mrs Jasper had gone out to work already, and he didn't know how to use a needle and thread, so he turned up the legs of his trousers and put on his jacket – only to find that the sleeves were much too long. He was very cross, and stamped his feet, but that didn't do any good, so he had to turn up the sleeves of his jacket. He ran outside and jumped into his car. "What is the matter with the car?" he cried. "My feet hardly reach the pedals!" But it wasn't the car that was at fault. Mr Jasper was growing quite small. He drove off to the office, keeping out of the way of policemen, who, if they had seen him, would have thought he was much too young to drive a car.

At the office, he climbed on to his chair and opened his big red book, but he couldn't do his sums at all. What was worse, he told the manager that he wouldn't even try unless he could have a lollipop.

"You're a very naughty boy!" said the manager. "I've been watching you for the past few weeks, and this business of growing younger every day has got to stop. You'd better stay away from here until you come to your senses."

So Mr Jasper had to stay at home on his own all day, because Mrs Jasper went out to work, and he didn't like it at all. He had nobody to play with. Soon Mrs Jasper had to give up her work to look after him, because he had become such a nuisance, spreading jam all over the nice clean tablecloths and throwing things about when he couldn't have his own way. "If only you had listened to me," Mrs Jasper said, "this wouldn't have happened. We were well enough as we were. Why did you have to wish such a foolish wish?"

Mr Jasper burst into tears and threw his rattle at her.

At once, Mrs Jasper was sorry for him. He was such a tiny, little boy by now. She picked him up in her arms and said, "There, there! I didn't mean it. Who's a koochy, koochy, koochy little choo, then?" And she tickled him under the chin to try to make him smile.

But it didn't make him smile. Do you know what it did? It made him sneeze. He sneezed and he sneezed and he sneezed, and every time he sneezed he grew a little bit. Mrs Jasper had to put him down after the fourteenth sneeze, because he was growing so heavy, and she had to keep running off to find him bigger clothes, because he kept bursting out of the ones he was wearing.

At the end of the day Mr Jasper was exactly the age he had been when he made his wish. And then he stopped sneezing.

"You see?" said Mrs Jasper. "I was quite right, wasn't I? Once you have made a wish or sneezed you can never stop them. So, in future, I advise you never to wish again."

Mr Jasper had to admit that she was right. He never made a wish like that again. Of course, he often sneezed, especially when the wind blew down the chimney, but that didn't matter, because it only made him a tiny bit older, just like it does to you or me or anybody else.

*   *   *

Follow-up Discussion
This story opens up the possibility for discussing wishes. Ask the children to imagine that they have everything they need, just like Mr Jasper. A fairy grants them three wishes. Would they wish for something

they did not need, something they already had or something for someone who is less fortunate than themselves? Discussion of the children's wishes could prove profitable.

Another follow-up topic that could result from this story is the problems that are faced by the elderly.

Language Development and Creative Writing
The three wishes can also be used in creative writing and classroom discussion.

Environmental Studies and Science
Growing things and studying life-cycles could be developments of this story.

Mathematics
The children could be involved in a long-term project on graphical representation of their heights, weights and other measurements. The writer has also had the children in his school weighing and measuring a baby at weekly intervals.

Drama
This story presents some technical problems for use as a play. The shrinking of the main character would be rather difficult to stage.

The Great Tug-of-War

(Teamwork, Concern for the Environment)

There once lived a lady named Elise, who had one desire – to be the richest woman in the world. She had a loving husband and a dear little baby, and they lived in a castle overlooking a great lake, but that was not enough for her; she must be richer than anyone else had ever been. She made no secret of her heart's desire, and in time it came to the ears of the wicked magician who lived on the opposite shore of the lake. He thought he could have a great deal of fun at the lady's expense, so one day he stepped across the lake in one giant stride and sat down in the castle garden to wait for her.

When she came out for her customary evening stroll he greeted her and told her who he was. "And can you really obtain anything you wish, by magic?" she asked.

"Anything," he replied, "for a price."

"And what price would you ask to make me the richest woman in the world?" she asked.

"First of all," he said, "I should ask for your castle and all that it contains."

She laughed. "But if you made me the richest woman in the world," she said, "I could buy as many castles as I wanted, so let us strike the bargain at once. The castle is yours."

"And all it contains?" said the magician.

"Certainly," she replied, thinking only of the wealth that was to be hers.

"Very well," replied the magician. "Lie down upon this bench and close your eyes. You will sleep until the moon strikes full upon your face, and then you will wake to find yourself rich beyond your dreams."

Elise lay down without another thought in her head but that of the wealth in store, and she fell asleep. The wicked magician laughed. He flung out his arms and shouted a dreadful incantation composed of good words spelt backwards, and immediately there appeared in the middle of the lake a huge floating island which shone with a ghostly light. Then the magician pointed with one hand to the castle and with the other hand to the island, and the castle and all it contained rose up in the air and flew over the head of the sleeping lady and landed on the island in the middle of the lake.

When the moon struck full on her face Elise awoke, and saw with delight that she was wearing a gown made of silver cloth, her feet were encased in golden slippers, on her hands, neck and head were the costliest jewels imaginable, and scattered around her on the grass were ornaments heavily encrusted with precious stones. She clapped her hands in delight, but then she thought, "All this is very well, but is there enough here to make me the richest woman in the world?"

The magician knew what she was thinking, and he directed her gaze towards the spot where the castle had stood, and she saw that in its place was a hill composed of solid gold, surmounted with a tip of the finest rubies. Without a doubt that made her rich beyond her dreams. She jumped to her feet. "I must tell my husband!" she cried. "Where is he?"

"Where else would he be but in the castle where he belongs?" jeered the magician.

"And my baby?" she cried. "What have you done with my baby?"

"Your baby is in the castle, too," said the magician. "All that the castle contained was part of our bargain, remember."

Elise became faint with apprehension. "Give me back my dear ones," she sobbed. "You know I didn't intend to part with *them*."

But the magician was enjoying his power and he showed her the floating island with the castle gleaming in the ghostly light. And she saw that the island was tethered to the mainland by a silken rope that stretched out across the water. "All you have to do," said the magician softly, "is to haul it in and it shall be yours again."

Without stopping to think what an impossible task it was, Elise laid hold of the rope and tugged with all her strength, but she soon knew that there was no hope of her ever being able to succeed. She fell down on her knees and begged the magician to relent, but he looked at her with scorn and stepped back to his domicile on the other side of the lake. He too, had a silken rope attached to the island, and he was so strong that with one hand he could prevent the island from being pulled to Elise's side of the lake.

All night long the poor lady wept in the garden, and when the sun arose she ran down to the road that skirted the castle garden. There she met all sorts of travellers: merchants going to the city, farmers moving their stock, housewives going to market, and idle people going nowhere in particular. "Help me!" she pleaded, pointing to the island. "I am the richest woman in the world and I will pay you well to help me pull on this silken rope and haul in my castle." She gave to one person a ring, and to another the jewel that lay on her breast, to another her coronet, her ear-rings, her brooches. The people took hold of the rope and pulled with all their might, but they could not move the island, so with a shrug they continued on their way, gloating over their costly gifts and giving no further thought to Elise, who stood weeping on the shore.

An idea came to her. "I will send for all the strongest men in the land to help me. I still have all my priceless ornaments to bargain with. There will be no lack of volunteers, I am sure." And she was right. As soon as the strongest men in the land heard of the offer they came flocking to the castle garden – the wrestlers, the giants, the athletes, all the most powerful men – and they laid hold of the silken rope and pulled until their hands were sore. Even they were no match for the strength of the magician.

In desperation Elise cried, "I can at least visit my husband and child. I will buy a boat and be rowed across to the island." But when she came down to the shore she saw that the lake was full of monsters, and every boat she launched was immediately gobbled up by them. When she went back to the castle garden she saw that in her absence the strong men had hacked away at the golden hill and carried off every particle of gold as well as the precious stones on top. Elise was alone, and all that was left of her enormous wealth was the gown she was wearing. What she did not know was that the strong men had been lured to the magician's side by promises of even greater wealth than they had already stolen from her.

For many days and nights the poor lady stood gazing across at the place where she knew her heart's treasure lay, for she was now a sadder and a wiser woman. At length her story became known throughout the world, and good people who pitied her began to flock to the place where she stood. They helped her to pull on the rope, but though the island began to move a little, their strength was not enough, for the magician was being assisted by his strong men now and they had little trouble in holding their own.

One thing, however, the magician did not know – that there were far more good people in the world than bad and greedy ones, and, as time went by, more and more of them came to Elise's aid. The more people who laid hold of the rope the longer it grew, and the stronger, and gradually the island was hauled nearer and nearer to the shore. The magician was furious, and he tried every trick he could think of to stop the good people from pulling, but none of them worked. The magician's strong men began to feel frightened. They ran off, scattering themselves to the far corners of the earth. Alone, the magician could not hold. He was pulled into the lake and was never seen again.

Elise was reunited with her husband and child. She sold her gown of silver, and with the money she received for it she made a most beautiful garden in the place where the hill of gold had stood. It was for the people who had helped her, and is still there to this day, although it is extremely difficult to find.

*　　*　　*

Follow-up Discussion
The story will probably benefit by some discussion beforehand about the reality that riches are not just measurable in money and material possessions. This introduction could emphasize the value that can be placed on the trees, flowers, birds and animals around us and the importance of having a family and friends.

After the story, the ending could be discussed – the triumph of good over evil, the combined efforts of the good people spreading panic among the wicked magician's strong men.

It could be pointed out that Elise only starts to get the support of the good after she has realized that her avarice was as evil as the magician's wiles.

Language Development and Creative Writing
There are several points that can be developed for language development and creative writing.

The children could discuss and write about those things in life that they regard as important, with emphasis on the natural rather than the man-made.

Discussion could be moved on to deal with those distasteful things in the world – litter, vandalism, acts of unkindness, fighting and lies. Perhaps the children could suggest ways of combating these things. "Out of the mouths of babes and sucklings thou hast perfected praise."

Environmental Studies
The family has been mentioned as one of the aspects of life that is valuable. The children could do some research into their own families. They could illustrate it with photographs of mother, father, brothers and sisters, grandparents, aunts, uncles and cousins. The children could construct their own family tree.

Art and Craft
The island and the castle would make a wonderful painting, as would the mountain of gold topped with precious stones.

Drama, Movement and Music
The story will adapt well for use as a play. The magician's dance and dreadful incantations will allow a child with some degree of exhibitionism to take part.

The tug-of-war could form the theme for a movement lesson. The children could make up their own magician's dance and incantations.

Piko and the Growing-up Fairy

(Consideration for Others, Kindness)

Did you ever hear about the Growing-up Fairy? Do you believe in the Growing-up Fairy? Some people do and some people don't. Let me tell you what happened to Piko.

One day the Growing-up Fairy flew into a school to listen to what the children were saying. She hadn't been there very long when she exclaimed to herself, "This won't do! Most of these children are very pleasant children indeed, but one or two of them are so rude and unkind that I must do something about it." So she opened her little purse and took out her magic gloves and put them on.

Down below was a boy called Piko, and sitting next to him was a girl whose name was Kita.

"Why did you have to come and sit next to me?" Piko asked crossly.

"Because I like you," said Kita.

"Well I don't like you," Piko said. "You're stupid. You can't understand anything properly and you're so clumsy that you can't even play games."

"I can't help that," said Kita patiently.

The Growing-up Fairy said to herself, "Unkind words – I know how to deal with them," and she touched Piko on the head. You haven't forgotten that she was wearing magic gloves, have you?

Piko didn't feel anything at all, but he shrank a little bit. Whenever a child says something unkind to another, he – or she – always shrinks a little bit if the Growing-up Fairy happens to be around; but when children are kind, the Growing-up Fairy smiles, and then the children grow. Most children grow all the time, although they can't feel themselves doing it. But Piko didn't grow at all. He just went on shrinking every time he said something unkind.

At first, nobody noticed, because it was only a centimetre at a time, but when he became too small for his clothes and he couldn't see over the top of his desk, the teachers were quite concerned. "Has anybody seen Piko?" they would say. "Has he come to school today?"

"Yes, yes!" the children would cry. "He's sitting in the waste paper basket," or "He's underneath the radiator, Miss!" And the teachers would shake their heads and click their tongues, because there's nothing that annoys a teacher more than a shrinking child.

One day, Piko's father came to the school and asked to see the Headmistress.

"What seems to be the trouble?" asked the Headmistress, noticing that Piko's father looked rather angry.

"It's Piko," was the reply. "He's getting smaller every day, and I demand to know what you are going to do about it."

"Well," said the Headmistress. "There's very little that we *can* do."

"Why not?" snapped Piko's father. "You can teach him how to read and write, so why can't you teach him how to grow?"

"We'll see what we can do," the Headmistress promised.

The teachers had a meeting to talk about Piko, and the Growing-up Fairy went along, too, but nobody saw her because she disguised herself as a curl of hair on the Headmistress's shoulder. Growing-up Fairies can disguise themselves as almost *anything*, so it's as well to be careful what you're about.

The teachers had the most curious opinions as to what was causing Piko to shrink. The Growing-up Fairy could hardly believe her ears when she heard what some of them had to say.

"Perhaps he's staying out in the rain too long."

"His shoes may be wearing thin."

"He's not *trying* hard enough."

The Growing-up Fairy couldn't listen any longer. She cried out as loud as she could, "*Piko will grow as he learns to be kind.*"

All the teachers looked at the Headmistress, for they thought it was she who had spoken. "What an interesting idea," they murmured.

Then the Headmistress suddenly remembered about the Growing-up Fairy, and she knew that she must be somewhere in the school, although she never for a moment suspected that she was hiding in her curls. "I will speak to Piko," she said.

At first, Piko would not believe what the Headmistress told him. He thought it was silly, so he just went on shrinking and shrinking, until there was very little left of him at all. And then, one day, when he was cleaning out the hamster's cage with a brush no bigger than your thumb, a big boy began to tease the hamster most cruelly and to say what a stupid creature she was for running around her wheel all day.

"Leave her alone!" cried Piko, for he knew now what it was like to be small and what it was like when people bigger than himself shouted and were cruel to him. "She can't help being a hamster and being kept in a cage!"

The Growing-up Fairy smiled as she hadn't smiled for a long time, and Piko barely had time to get out of the cage before he grew quite big. "I'm growing!" he thought. "The Headmistress must be right!" For he had also noticed that the big boy had shrunk a little bit for his unkindness.

Piko went to Kita and said, "You can sit next to me if you like."

Kita was pleased. "Will you teach me how to play games?" she asked.

"Yes," said Piko.

And he went on growing. He grew and grew until he was quite grown up, and he never forgot the Growing-up Fairy. To this very day he still believes in her. What about you?

*   *   *

Follow-up Discussion

The obvious discussion that should be stimulated by this story is about the effects of unkindness. The children in this age group are both guilty of unkindness, in actions and speech, and susceptible to it. They will be able to relate easily to this story.

The concept that one shrinks when one is unkind is not far from the truth. One has only got to consider the shrinking feeling one experiences when one is the victim of unkindness or unpleasantness. "I felt about this size" is a commonly used phrase when we are talking about being embarrassed.

Language Development and Creative Writing

Imagining that they are as small as a hamster and discussing their view of the things about them could produce some fruitful language and creative writing activities. What would be the advantages and disadvantages of being very small?

Environmental Studies and Science
The story provides an opening for looking at and researching the opposite of shrinking, growth. A balanced diet is necessary for a healthy life. What is a balanced diet? Certain ingredients in our diet assist our growth, warmth, cell repair or just keep us healthy. The children could research into the functions of the various foods we eat and the effects of eating too much of some foods.

Art and Craft
There is a rich fund of stories about small people like Tom Thumb and Mrs Pepperpot. The children could make furniture for a small person, using materials from the bits and pieces box.

Drama and Movement
This story does present problems for adaptation into a play. As with "The Wish That Came True", the problem is shrinking the main character. The story is likely to have an impact on the children in the age range and should be read by a teacher or a good reader to the assembly.

Items from the dressing-up box are normally from grown-up wardrobes. The children enjoy wearing them in spite of the problems they present for walking. Walking in large shoes could be developed as a theme for a movement lesson.

The Amazing Washerwoman

(Cheerfulness in Adversity, Unselfishness)

The amazing washerwoman lived all by herself in a cottage on the outskirts of a village. Nobody knew when she had first come there, and *she* wouldn't tell them, but of one thing everybody was certain; she was very happy in her work.

All day long, from early morning until late at night, she could be heard singing over her tub. Strange songs they were, too, that she sang to herself, made up out of her own head, and it was said that whatever she sang when she was washing the clothes was washed right into them, like a witch's charm.

It was quite natural, then, that when people brought their washing to her, they would say, "Be sure to wash some happiness into our clothes," and the old woman would nod, and smile, and say that she couldn't promise anything but that she would do her best. All the same, people began to believe that she *could* wash happiness into their clothes, and soon her fame spread far and wide.

One day a lady drove up to the cottage. "Are you the amazing washerwoman who washes charms into clothes?" she enquired.

"That's what people say," replied the washerwoman.

The lady, who was rather plain, handed her washing to the washerwoman and said, "Wash my gowns for me, please, and if you can, wash some beauty into them."

The washerwoman made her usual reply, and when the lady had gone she said to herself, "It is a harmless vanity," and then she got out her tub and poured hot water into it. She smiled as she began to wash the clothes, and this is what she sang:

"Plunge the clothes into the tub,
Turn and toss them, scrub, scrub, scrub;
As one is plain that would be fairer,
Wash in beauty to the wearer."

Then she dried the washing, ironed it, and when the lady called next morning her gowns were ready for her. The lady took them back home as fast as she could and hastily put on her favourite gown. When she appeared in it before her friends, they were quite astonished. "Why, how beautiful she is in that gown!" they cried. And the lady had to admit that she had asked the amazing washerwoman to wash beauty into her clothes. And after that, all the ladies for miles around brought their washing to the amazing washerwoman, and, strangely enough, they all seemed more beautiful after she had washed it.

The gentlemen, too, were curious about the old washerwoman. One day, a gentleman brought his washing to her. He was exceedingly thin, and in those days it was the fashion to be stout, so he asked her if she could do anything for him. "For you see," he confessed, "I have grown thin since my clothes were made for me, and now they hang on me like corn sacks, and everybody laughs at me. I should dearly love to be stout again."

"I cannot promise anything," said the amazing washerwoman, "but I will do my best, for it is a harmless vanity."

When he had left her, she got out her tub and poured hot water into it and put in the gentleman's clothes. And she sang:

"Plunge the clothes into the tub,
Turn and toss them, scrub, scrub, scrub;
As one is lean that should be stout,
Wash until he fills them out."

When the gentleman put on his clothes the next day, they fitted him perfectly, and he couldn't help confiding his secret to his wife, who told it to her maid, who told it in confidence to three of her friends, and so it got about that it was the amazing washerwoman who had made the gentleman stout.

People began to wonder if she could wash anything she chose into her washing, just by singing a rhyme over it, and so it happened that one dark night there came a tap-tap-tap at the washerwoman's door. When she opened it, there stood a man with a bundle of clothes. "Will you wash my clothes for me, washerwoman?" he whispered.

She looked at him with her dark, shrewd eyes. "Why do you come by night?" she asked. "And why do you speak in a whisper?"

"That's my affair," he hissed. "Will you wash my clothes?"

"Certainly," she said, "but what is it you want me to wash into them?"

"I want to be rich," he replied. "I want my neighbour's house and my neighbour's money and my neighbour's land. Can you do it for me?"

The amazing washerwoman said, "I never promise anything, but I will do my best." The man disappeared into the darkness and the washerwoman got out her tub and filled it with hot water, then she began to sing:

"Plunge the clothes into the tub,
Turn and toss them, scrub, scrub, scrub;
As one there is who covets riches,
Wash contentment into his breeches."

The man was back before the break of day, and so anxious was he to see if the amazing washerwoman's charm had worked, that he did not wait to carry his washing back home, but put on his clean clothes in her kitchen.

As he walked home to his house in the next valley he saw the sun come up. He saw it shining on the roof of his house and on his little plot of land, and on his apple trees. He said to himself, "Why do I want to be rich? I have everything I need here. I am perfectly content to be as I am."

And so he was. The amazing washerwoman disappeared shortly after that, and though many people tried to find her, nobody ever could.

*   *   *

Follow-up Discussion
The washerwoman has truly amazing powers. If the children had taken their clothes to her, what would they have asked to be washed into them? This question could be asked of the children and their replies could be discussed as a forum led by a panel of teachers. The distinction between tangible and intangible desires could be explained and discussed. The children could be encouraged to try to ask for things that are unselfish.

Language Development and Creative Writing
The children could talk about people who are less fortunate than themselves – the homeless, the disabled and the under-nourished.

Some of the older pupils might be able to write some short poems like the ones in the story.

Environmental Studies and Science
The question of washing clothes could provide an opening for children to do some research into the differences between different brands of powders and detergents. Using measured amounts, they could compare the amounts of suds each produces. They will also be able to discuss the feel of the suds on their hands. Squares cut from an old sheet could be soiled with different substances and washed in the different products, to see if the makers' claims are true.

Art and Craft
Washing hanging on a line, dancing in the breeze, would make an interesting and colourful painting.

Drama and Movement
This story will adapt well for use in assembly.

In a movement lesson the children could mime a sequence of washing clothes prior to the invention of the washing machine.

The Wonderful Washing Machine

(Caring and Sharing)

Mrs Lenska filled up the washing machine with water and when she went to put the clothes in she stared in amazement. "Come here, Henry," she called to Mr Lenska. "Come and see what's happened to the washing machine."

Mr Lenska had a good look. "It seems to be full of strawberry jam," he said at last. "Mm – smells like strawberry jam, too, *tastes* like strawberry jam. It *is* strawberry jam." He looked sternly at Mrs Lenska. "What have you been doing?" he demanded.

"Nothing," she returned, "except fill it up with water. I don't know how it happened."

"I expect it was those kids from the next apartment," Mr Lenska said. "They're always up to some trick or other."

"It couldn't be them," Mrs Lenska said. "They're away at summer camp. Besides, I haven't opened the door to anyone all morning."

"Well, what are we going to do about it?" asked Mr Lenska. "It's perfectly good jam, but we can't eat that much."

"We'll keep a few pounds of it," Mrs Lenska decided, "and put the rest down the waste disposal. There's nothing else we can do."

So they cleared out the jam and then they cleaned out the washing machine with fresh water, and it was soon working perfectly again. All went well for a few weeks, and then Mrs Lenska noticed something wrong again.

"Henry," she said, "the washing machine's gone peculiar again."

Mr Lenska groaned. "Not more strawberry jam?" he said.

"No," she replied. "This time it seems to be chocolate sauce."

"That's not possible," said Mr Lenska.

"Possible or not," Mrs Lenska retorted, "that's what it is. Taste it and see."

He tasted it, and it was.

"This is ridiculous," he said, "but I'm due in town in an hour's time. I can't stay to help you clean it out this time, but I'll call in and ask the engineer to come and take a look at it."

When the engineer arrived he said it certainly was chocolate sauce, but he didn't seem too surprised. "Would you mind telling me," he asked Mrs Lenska, "where you bought this machine?"

"I exchanged it for my mahogany table," she told him.

"With Mrs Kalman downstairs?"

"That's right – how did you know?"

"I've been called to this machine before," he replied. "It's had at least five owners to my knowledge. Nobody seems to know what to do with it when it starts behaving like this."

Mrs Lenska was annoyed. "I think Mrs Kalman might have warned me," she said. "After all, my mahogany table doesn't do peculiar things." She glared at the engineer. "Can you fix it?" she asked.

"Well, I'll have a look at it," he said, "but I don't hold out much hope of being able to alter it. Most of the time it works normally, and then something seems to change it altogether." He smiled sadly. "I think it must be magic," he added.

"Magic!" snapped Mrs Lenska scornfully. "There never was any such thing."

"Of course not," murmured the engineer.

He checked all the valves and all the switches; he tried out the motor; he looked at the joints connecting the water to the machine; he even read the instructions on the washing powder packet; but he could find nothing wrong at all.

"That settles it," said Mrs Lenska. "I shall just have to buy a new one. I was saving for something else, but this is more important."

"Are you sure," asked the engineer, "that you can't find a use for this one?"

"Quite sure," she replied. "What on earth could I do with all that strawberry jam and chocolate sauce?"

The engineer shook his head. "What does Mr Lenska think about it?" he enquired.

"Henry thinks exactly as I do," was the answer. "He thinks it's a nuisance and a bad bargain."

"In that case," said the engineer, "I'll tell you what I'll do. I'll ask around. There may be somebody who'd know what to do with it."

"Do that," said Mrs Lenska.

A few weeks later the engineer called again. "Did you buy a new washing machine?" he asked.

"Yes," said Mrs Lenska, "and I haven't had a single problem with it. I can't think why I put up with the other one for so long."

"Have you still got the old one?" asked the engineer.

"Yes," she said. "Have you found someone to take it off my hands?"

"I think so, if you will take a portable TV for it. Mrs Slinger in the next block is willing to do a deal. She says your old washing machine is exactly what she has been looking for."

Mrs Lenska said, "Henry, go with the man and take a look at Mrs Slinger's portable TV. If it's okay we'll let her have the old washing machine for it."

An hour later the deal was fixed. Mrs Lenska did her washing and watched TV at the same time. She never gave her old washing machine a second thought.

In the next apartment block Mrs Slinger was watching the washing machine with great interest. "I do believe it's vegetable soup!" she cried. "Delicious!" and she and Mr Slinger and the little Slingers had vegetable soup for lunch. When they had finished there was still a lot left. "Go and knock all the doors in the block," she said, "and tell them there's free soup at the Slingers'. Tell them to bring their own basins."

In no time at all the soup had been gladly received and all that remained to be done was rinse out the washing machine with hot water. After that the machine worked normally for quite a long time, which was a good thing, because Mr and Mrs Slinger had a lot of children and a lot of washing to do, but every once in a while it produced something special – custard, or lemonade, or broth, or ice cream, and always Mrs Slinger shared it out among her neighbours. It never once occurred to her to throw the surplus away.

The engineer called one day. "How are you getting on with the washing machine?" he enquired.

"Fine!" said Mrs Slinger, and explained what was happening and how she was dealing with it.

"I'm glad of that," said the engineer. "I always knew that one day, sooner or later, somebody would know what to do with it."

*   *   *

Follow-up Discussion

The old motto "Waste not want not" is well-illustrated in this story. The children can learn that waste of any sort, particularly of food, is terrible. Children could discuss and record different ways of being thrifty.

Another important discussion point that can be developed in follow-up to this story is sharing. This could include aid that is given to under-developed and under-nourished countries. These points are often highlighted by TV programmes like *Blue Peter*, so some of the children will have some knowledge of these problems.

Language Development and Creative Writing

The children could discuss or write about what they would like the washing machine to make. The magical powers of the machine could be extended, to include changing things the children do not like into their favourite dishes.

Environmental Studies and Science

The children could be encouraged to collect labels from different foods, to determine the countries of origin. This could lead naturally into a study of the major food-producing countries of the world and their major harvest, exports, climatic conditions.

Art and Craft

A large map of the world could be painted and put up on the wall. The origins of the products could be indicated on the map with coloured words.

Drama, Movement and Music

This story will adapt for use as a play but, as the moral implications of the story are so important, it might be felt that greater impact will be gained by reading the story.

Harvesting different crops could provide some useful movement exercises and help the children to understand the hardship experienced by some of the slaves in America and other parts of the world.

Some of the Negro songs from America are about harvesting and could be introduced.

PART TWO

CHAPTER FIVE

Some Suggestions for Extended Follow-Up Work

In this chapter I have grouped some of the stories together under six thematic headings. The follow-up activities suggested in Chapters 1–4 are intended to be stimulated by each story. But the stories can, of course, be used in connection with projects that are already in progress, and the activities which I am introducing in this chapter are an attempt to help teachers to involve children in different aspects of in-depth research.

Three of the following groups of stories have suggested follow-up which is of a scientific nature. I have concentrated on science, because of the criticism that has been levelled at teachers in the primary and first school sectors, by the H.M.I. in the Primary and First Schools Reports. The science work I am outlining does not require any specialist scientific knowledge or apparatus. If properly supervised, all the activities are perfectly safe, which makes them ideal for use with children in the 5 to 11 age group.

GROUP I

The Cake That Made People Jump
Margery Moonlight and the Magic Party
Food From The Forest
The Wish That Came True
Piko and the Growing-up Fairy
The Boy Who Couldn't Tell The Truth

These stories are all linked by the subject of "Food". "The Cake That Made People Jump", "Margery Moonlight", "Food from the Forest" and "The Boy Who Couldn't Tell The Truth" suggest the preparation of food. "Piko" and "The Wish that Came True" open up the possibility for study and research into "Balanced Diet".

FOOD
In "The Cake That Made People Jump" Mrs Jenkins uses a most unscientific method of baking her cakes, yet when we bake we are directly involved with many scientific processes.

A baking lesson will give the children their first experiences of scientific activities in an exciting and practical way. The children are presented with problems which will need to be solved by investigation and experimentation. All the senses are brought into play. Some of the study skills that will be introduced include observation, questioning, experimenting, and making predictions and deductions.

With supervision, the children could bake a cake, which will involve them in weighing, measuring, timing and following the instructions of the recipe. They will be observing all the changes that take place during the baking process.

The ingredients used and the baking process provide many opportunities to introduce further scientific discussion. Just cracking the egg into a saucer can be followed up by drawing the children's attention to the different parts of the egg. The teacher can talk about the functions played by the yolk, the white, the membrane and the shell in incubation. The milk, the flour, and the sugar similarly provide the opening for scientific discussion.

Baking bread introduces another ingredient that will be of interest to the children – yeast. Mix the yeast with sugar and watch it gradually turn into a liquid. This will provide the teacher with further opportunity for introducing an explanation and discussion. When the dough is placed in a warm place to prove, what happens to it? It rises to almost double its size – another valuable stimulus for scientific teaching.

On one occasion I turned my school into a bakery for a day. It was organized as a drama lesson, with the aim of developing and initiating the use of language. The older children were told that they were married with a family to support but they were unemployed. The opening of a new bakery in the area provided them with the opportunity to gain employment. They had to attend a realistic interview in which the children were asked the type of questions a prospective employer might ask. They were then given a step-by-step lesson in baking bread, during which they took down the recipe and notes of the baking instructions. The older children took charge of a small group of younger ones and they worked together to bake their bread. While they were doing this, it was announced that the firm had won a prestigious order to supply the bread buns for the Royal Wedding reception. Each group attempted to produce the most original confectionery as a tribute to Prince Charles and Lady Diana.

While the bread was in the oven, the bakery came under the scrutiny of an auditor and work study team. Rumours of mechanization and resultant unemployment were rife. A meeting of senior employees was called to discuss the situation. Without any prompting from the adults involved, the children came up with a way of saving their jobs. It meant pooling their savings and investing them into the firm – their own version of a workers' cooperative. The language that was used throughout was mature and exciting, which can be witnessed from the video tape that we made of the day.

Up to this point, I have only mentioned the scientific potential presented by baking. Other aspects of cookery also offer possibilities for further work with science. Melting butter and cheese, boiling water, evaporation and condensation involve states of matter. Rice can be boiled in water to show absorption, and making toast illustrates the effects of burning.

In the other two stories in this group, Piko and Mr Jasper shrink – which poses the question, "What makes you grow?" This can be developed into a study of diet. Carbohydrates, fats, vitamins and proteins perform different functions in maintaining a healthy body. The essential trace elements and roughage are also important ingredients of a healthy, balanced diet. This is a subject for which there is a wealth of published material, which will help both the teacher and the children to make this into an interesting project.

GROUP II

Sam Snuffett
The Princess and the Rainbow
The Silver Dollar

The common link between these stories is "Light". This subject can be extended to include "Rainbows" and "Reflections".

LIGHT
Probably one of the first and most important discoveries early man ever made was learning to light a fire. This discovery not only provided a source of heat and a means of preparing food; it also meant that man had a means of lighting his dwelling after sunset.

The oil lamp stood the test of time, remaining almost unchanged for 15,000 years. The Romans used candles made of melted fats and waxes. These were expensive beyond the means of the poor. The fuels used to produce light varied according to the availability of inflammable materials. In the warmer climates where vegetable oils were plentiful, oil of the olive and sesame provided illumination. The people from colder countries which did not support oil-producing fruit and vegetables used animal fats such as seal and whale blubber.

The inflammable oils also made it possible for early man to use a torch. The Olympic torch which today symbolizes the opening of the modern games has its origins in the baton that was passed from runner to runner in the relay races in the original games.

The history of the development of the electric light is a well-documented subject and could be researched using the source material available.

Working with batteries, wire, switches, bulbs and bulb holders can give the children practical experience of making the bulb light up. Simple circuit diagrams should be drawn and the children encouraged to learn how to follow them. The first diagrams should have the words and drawings of the battery, the switch and the bulb. When the children have come to realize that the circuit must be completed for the bulb to light, the circuit should be drawn with the conventional circuitry symbols, to see whether the children can work out what the symbols stand for. More sophisticated circuits could be introduced by including bulb holders with flasher units, so that the children can make working models of lighthouses and traffic lights.

Another natural development from working with light would be to look at the spectrum. Children always make some remark when they see a rainbow. The rainbow provides a starting point for discussing what white light is. Using a prism and a strong light, a spectrum can be projected onto a piece of white card. The seven colours of the spectrum can be indicated – red, orange, yellow, green, blue, indigo and violet. The order of the spectrum is the subject of mnemonics, for example: "Richard Of York Gave Battle In Vain". Can the children find other examples or make up their own?

The children can do some simple experiments with a torch and acetate sheets of different colours of the rainbow. The red sheet will only allow red light to pass through, all the other colours being absorbed. The same principle applies to looking at the colours of flowers. Take a red rose into a darkened room and shine a torch onto it. What colour is the rose? Now cover the glass of the torch with a blue acetate sheet or blue paint and repeat the operation. What colour is the rose now?

A wide range of activities can be enjoyed with reflections, which is yet another progression that we can explore when we are studying light. A mirror can be used to discover symmetrical shapes. Squares, rectangles, circles, different triangles and many-sided shapes can be provided for the children. Which of the shapes is symmetrical? Have any of the shapes more than one axis of symmetry? This leads into a fascinating search for palindromes, like TOOT and OXO.

The children can be encouraged to make a collection of reflectors. To begin with, the children will tend to concentrate on surfaces that reflect a clear image. They may have to be persuaded to look for other reflective surfaces, such as road signs and the road safety products that children should be encouraged to wear at night.

Two mirrors can be hinged with sticky tape so that they can be opened at different angles and a drinking straw is stretched between their bases. The straw is reflected in the mirrors and the reflections form a series of geometrical shapes depending upon the angles at which the two mirrors are held. What happens to the shape as you increase and decrease the angle of the mirrors? This exercise can be extended by using more straws placed in different shapes, like a square bisected twice to make four squares, and then with diagonals placed in position. The mirrors are opened and closed as before. The number of mirrors can be gradually increased to make a range of kaleidoscopes. The mathematical language that can be developed from this will be profitable.

Those children who have been to a hall of mirrors can talk about the distorted images they saw of themselves. This can lead into introducing the children to the concept of concave and convex mirrors and lenses. An old pair of spectacles would be a useful aid to help the children understand the concept.

So far we have only mentioned activities that are classroom-based. Work connected with light, rainbows and reflections can equally profitably be done out of doors. The rainbow effect of oil on a puddle, reflections in a pond or river, and the concentration of the sun's rays to create heat are just a few possible starting points.

GROUP III

The Children of Mulberry School
The Boy Who Couldn't Tell The Truth

Two extended research projects can result from these stories. Firstly, the stories suggest an environmental study based on the school and the immediate environment. The other project involves research into children's games and playground culture.

ABOUT MY SCHOOL
When children are sitting in school, they tend to be totally unaware of the fact that there is a wide range of activities going on outside.

Probably the best way to correct this would be to do a concentric environmental study starting with the classroom. Draw a map with the school at the very centre. Initially, the map is blank apart from the central point. Start with all the people in school who directly affect the running of the school. Where do they come from? Remember that, apart from the other members of staff, the headteacher, the kitchen staff, the school secretary and the caretaker, there are many others who either work on a part-time basis, like the "lollipop" person, or visit the school, such as the milkman, the postman and the gardener. We are now beginning to get a picture of the school and its links with the local community. Until young children have a clear understanding of their position in the locality, it is pointless trying to introduce them to a broader geographical study.

A study of the school can involve the children in some very profitable mathematical work in the form of sets, number, measuring and geometry. How many boys and girls are there in my class? When are their birthdays? How old are they in years and months? All this information can be displayed attractively in the form of simple graphs. This information can then be gathered from the school as a whole.

The routine of the school day or week also provides plenty of opportunity for number work. How many children have school meals? How many children are absent? Division crops up when the children look at the way in which the classes share the use of the hall, the television, the music and P.E. equipment.

Recording different times which are important to the class and school programme can help to give the children some meaning to the practice of telling the time, as well as being an exercise in sequencing events. The children can time themselves and others as they tackle different tasks.

Experience of volume and capacity can be gained by starting with the school milk bottle. How much milk do you drink in a week, a month or a year? Conservation of capacity can be explored by pouring liquid from the milk bottle into different containers. It is important that the children are encouraged to use the correct vocabulary – taller, longer, higher, shorter and the same as.

Now that the children have researched the school and its immediate surroundings, they can begin to broaden the area of study. Where do the supplies of the foodstuffs for the school meals come from? The advisors who visit the school may well have been recruited from other parts of the country. If the school secretary can be persuaded to let the children have the stamps and postmarks from all the mail entering the school, the children will be able to build up a picture of their position in the country as a whole.

An important concept that even escapes some of the older children is that most of the jobs people do involve some degree of training. The children could be encouraged to draw up a questionnaire to discover what was involved in learning how to become "a cook" or "a postman". This could be used with as many of the people with whom they come into contact as are prepared to answer their questions.

Tracing the history of the school would involve both the children and the teacher working together as investigators. The school could be researched through the log book and the admissions register. In the case of older schools, some of the children may discover parents and other relatives who have attended the school. Parents, grandparents and other elderly people might be encouraged to come into school to talk about and answer questions about their own schooldays. I have done this in my own school and the dialogue between the generations was both interesting and mutually rewarding. It was just another example of the close affinity that exists between these two generations.

Additional information about the school may be obtained from back copies of your local newspapers which should be lodged with the reference library. Old photographs of schoolchildren through the ages could provide some discussion about the changes in fashions. The children might re-enact school life of a past age. This can be a very rewarding exercise and it might help them to appreciate how lucky they are to be going to school nowadays rather than in the past.

CHILDREN'S GAMES AND PLAYGROUND CULTURE

All over the world, children play games. The apparatus required to provide enjoyment ranges from a few stones to the sophisticated electronic equipment of today. Again, it is felt that the best starting point would be a study of the games that the children play in their own playground. It is also important that the children be made to think to both the past and the future. There are lots of seasonal games that will be out of season at present. Conkers will not be in vogue in January, just as the children would not be building snowmen and throwing snowballs in June.

The study can be further broadened to include games from other parts of Britain and then extended to other parts of the world. This could involve the children in writing letters to other schools to gather their information. It might even encourage correspondence on a longer term.

Many traditional games like marbles, five stones and hopscotch have strict rules. These rules have regional variations which could be researched. The children have different ways of deciding who is "on" or "it". Through the letters the children write, a collection of variations in the rules and elimination rhymes could be gathered.

The fact that traditional games have survived in the face of competition from modern computerized games is a testimony that playground culture still exists. Ask the children to consider how they learnt to play all the different games. Who taught them the rules and elimination rhymes? In the majority of cases, they will have been handed down from one generation of children to the next without any influence or intervention from adults.

So many skills, of language and of mathematics, as well as the social ones, are involved in the games children play. Take "hide and seek" as an example. The children have to learn to count before they can join in. The count is an arbitrary unit of time and the children learn terminology connected with time. They will use language like "That was too short. I need a longer time to hide."

In schools where children from other countries attend, the influence of those countries might become evident in some of the games played in the playground. What might also become evident is the close relationship between some of the games. Hopscotch and Golden Man (from Pakistan) have obvious similarities.

Skipping is another traditional game that has stood the test of time. Thanks to television's coverage of boxers in training, it is no longer just a girl's game. There are countless skipping rhymes which have to be memorized, which is an exercise in language development and number. Similarly, ball games involving bouncing and catching have traditional counting with rhythm songs to accompany them, such as "salt, mustard, vinegar, pepper".

Playground games alone provide scope for an extensive research project, but this can be extended to include indoor games. Traditional paper and pencil, card and board games can also be studied. Toy manufacturers are making a healthy living by producing electronic and plastic versions of games that can be played and enjoyed just as much using paper and pencil. Battleships, Make a Square and Connect Four are just three examples.

Games are an important part of growing up and learning how to cope with adulthood. In order to play the game and to derive enjoyment from it, everybody has got to play according to the rules.

GROUP IV

The Boy Who Couldn't Tell The Truth
The Children of Mulberry School
Jeremy Jumbletop
The Terrible Traffic Jam
The Man Who Mended Dolls
The Teddy Minders
The Honky-Tonk Piano
Marna's Paper Bag
Mrs Tippett and the Yellow Blanket
The Amazing Washerwoman
The Wonderful Washing Machine

All these stories can be used in connection with a project on "People Who Work for Us".

PEOPLE WHO WORK FOR US

I am a firm believer in starting with the child and its immediate environment and working out from there in a concentric study. This must be evident from the studies into "My School" and "Children's Games". I intend to deal with the "People Who Work for Us" project in exactly the same way, particularly as there are aspects of the "My School" project that are duplicated here.

All the initial research into the people who have a direct influence on the child's life in school should become the starting point for this topic. On this occasion, the emphasis should be more on what these people do, rather than on where they come from.

I feel that, once again, the children should research the training the people received to qualify them for the positions they hold. This may help the children to realize that people do not just leave school and drop into a job, which is a view held by many pupils, even in high schools.

Once again, we should try to devise a simple questionnaire to help the children collect their data. With the teacher's help, the questionnaire can be made short enough so that it can be administered without causing too much inconvenience to the person answering it.

The study is broadened to include visitors coming to the school – the school doctor, nurse and dentist. "The Terrible Traffic Jam", "Mrs Tippett", "Marna's Paper Bag" and "Jeremy Jumbletop" introduce the children to people who provide either an emergency or an essential service. People like the policeman, the ambulance driver, the fireman, nurses, doctors, home helps and the coast guard are from the emergency or social services. The men who maintain the supplies of electricity, gas and water, and those who see to the removal of sewage and refuse, as well as the postman and milkman, can be included in the essential services. The topic can be widened even further to include all the shops and traders who supply us with the commodities that are essential to life. This could include the dolls' hospital as suggested by "The Man Who Mended Dolls".

This is a vast topic and one for which there is no shortage of back-up material.

GROUP V

Three Monsters
The Terrible Scary Hairy Monster

Monsters are part of a child's early life and most children enjoy being frightened by them. They also enjoy trying to frighten others. A project on "Monsters" is a potential success, but care must be taken and it must be very thoughtfully planned in advance. If this project is not structured, it could, in itself, develop into an uncontrollable monster.

Structured play with the teacher taking part would be a suitable starting point. The contents of the dressing-up box might reveal the costumes you require. The two stories could be dramatized either as straight plays or in the form of puppet plays. They would provide the vehicle for structured play. Language could be developed by discussing what the children expect their monsters to look like. They will have their own ideas of what monsters are, from watching television programmes like *Dr Who*, *Blake's Seven* and *The Muppets*. They can discuss whether they would prefer their monsters to be the horrific Dr Who-type or the loveable Muppet monsters.

The project can be developed in two directions, either upwards in size to a study of dinosaurs, which is another favourite topic, or downwards to include the small creatures which *Science 5–13*, published by Macdonald Educational, entitled "Minibeasts". Both these topics have sufficient back-up resource material to make them very extensive studies.

GROUP VI

WEATHER AND THE SEASONS

All the stories in Chapter Two will find a place in projects that are already a regular feature of the school calendar. These are also topics that have so much back-up material that a whole chapter could be devoted just to publications on "Weather and the Seasons".

1 Announcing Byrness First School's production of "Father Christmas and the Ice Goblins".

2 Gnomes loading the sleigh. Father Christmas's cave is in the background.

CHAPTER SIX

Some Examples of Work Stimulated by the Stories

3 Ice goblins creeping in.

My school is a small rural first school in Northumberland. It is situated on the edge of the Border Forest, the largest man-made forest in Europe, and twelve miles from the recently completed Kielder Water which is Europe's largest man-made lake.

The school has just under twenty children and I have used them to market research the stories for the book. Joy Brooks, an advisor from Nuneaton, was recruited to read the stories and to comment on them. Joy and I expressed some doubts about the suitability of some of the stories, but my children persuaded me that all of them were eminently suitable, so I have acted upon their advice and they have been included.

It would have been unethical of me to suggest that these stories could be used in a particular way without first attempting it myself. The stories have been used for language development and creative writing and they have stimulated pleasing results.

We also used "Father Christmas and the Ice Goblins" as a play for part of our Christmas Carol Concert in 1982. We do not have a stage or staging units and our hall is quite small. Using very basic scenery, we created two scenes from the play. In one corner of the hall we made Father Christmas's cave, using a table standing on four desks. The whole structure was covered with a white dust sheet and decorated to give the impression of glittering frost. In the other corner of the hall we constructed the children's bedroom with the Wendy house.

We recruited parents and friends to help make the costumes. We always get a good response to calls for help in situations like this; and it results in some very original ideas being incorporated into the costume design. I have taken some photographs of the children in their costumes at the dress rehearsals. Some of these photographs are included here. They give a clear indication of the scale of production that these stories can be adapted for, even in a small school with limited resources.

All the stories have been used to stimulate language. They have produced some original and beautifully phrased descriptive responses, even from the rising 5-year-olds. I am including examples of creative writing that has resulted from seven of the stories.

"The Children of Mulberry School" produced two quite long stories by twin girls, aged 8. They show how children's minds work when they imagine what naughty children really do.

"Mr Murphy's Gnomes" was told to the children under the glare of television lights when the local independent television crew came to school to film a day in the life of a rural school. The children were told to imagine that they were one of the gnomes and to write about a night's adventure when they came to life.

After being told "Fine Feathers" the children were encouraged to put themselves in the place of the sparrow and to imagine what bird they would like to be changed into. Linda's sense of humour has had a profound effect on Kim and her story reflects this.

"The Teddy Bears' Picnic" was followed by a discussion about hearing noises in the house at night. This resulted in the stories about investigating noises heard downstairs on a sleepless night.

When we read "The Three Monsters", we discussed bravery and heroism and the children contributed to a long list of people who have exhibited bravery without resorting to aggression or force. Each child was then told to research one of the people from the list and to write a story about that person in the first person.

From Chapter Four I have included some examples of creative writing from "The Good Fairies" and "The Wish That Came True".

Probably the best recommendation for all these stories as stimuli for creative writing is the number of examples of reasonable stories from Scott. Scott is an 8-year-old twin, whose brother is Craig. His stories in the past have been unimaginative but it can be seen that Linda's stories have fired his imagination and he has written about things other than war games and shooting his brother with a bren gun which was his normal style.

All the work included in this chapter is as it was written by the children. The work was not corrected, and therefore stands as examples of the children's own free expression.

The Children of Mulberry School

Naughty Naughty

Once upon a time in Bristol there was a small school. It was a very nice school with a small river trickling past the yard.

Well let me tell you about the children. Well I am disgusted to tell you but I will. The children were dreadful. "Oh gosh!" One day the headmaster said "Today I have bought an extra strong belt. It might shut them up. but he was wronge. As he went into the hall a bucket of water came down on him "splash" "Help Help" he cried

with madness "Oh dear" he said "you need a lesoon" he cried. At night he would always go into the boys and girls rooms and put out the lights. One night he went in they were all having pillow fights. He stood there as if he was paralysed and shook his head. Suddenly someone threw a pillow right in his mouth and worst of all it had a hole in and all the feathers went down his throat. The next day in maths he was coughing and spluttring. One Thursday the day they did P.E. they played hocky. We don't like hockey We want to play football, O.K. "No" you can't said the teacher in a shrill voice. "Yes we can" and they started throwing the hockey sticks down. You can't its "Government property". The clock chimed bong, bong, bong. "It is dinner time" called Mrs Jelly top Mrs Inkfingers was the dinner lady. For dinner it was mushy peas. All the children threw the peas in Mrs Inkfingers mouth. "Oh we don't like peas either do we so we are giving them to you." Next it was sticky jam pudding. Horrid they said and threw it on the wall and because it was sticky it stuck to the wall. "Oh you need to be taught a lesoon" she said. I will tell the "head master". "Ah"! he said in a happy voice. "I know." Next day in the hall he said now the school is going to be shut down. A great clapping came from the hall. The hall shook when the children came back. They had learnt their lesoon. From then on they were good and on open day every one said what well behaved children.
(*Clio, aged 8*)

Naughty School

Once upon a time in Devon there was a very nice school except for one thing. All the childre were badly behaved. They screamed, they shouted, and did all nasty things. Then one morning the head master said "I am going to try to control those children but I don't think I will succeed. So when they went into the hall the head master said "We will sing some hymns but when he went to get the hymn books there were not there. The head master said "I will have to get some more." The children started to throw tomatoes at the head master. He said "I cannot stand any more I will have to think of something and teach them a lesson." When the head master went home he said to his wife "I will have to think of something to control those children." When the head master went to bed he thought all night on a plan. In the morning he said to his wife "I do not want to go to school today but I will have to go." When the head master got through the school gates he started to

slip and slide. The children had put tar on the drive. "Crash"! The car went straight into the wood. When the head master got into school all the children were tearing the register up. The head master was furious and said we will play tennis. And he went to get the tennis balls and the tennis rackets. The head master said "Kim and Craig can play first". They got the tennis balls and tennis rackets. Kim served first. Craig missed it and it went bonk on the head masters head. Then Kim and Craig went up to the head master and smashed the tennis rackets on his head. He was mad. He said I have just had enough, you had better go inside and have lunch. When they went inside they went into the dinner hall. It was soup. All the children flicked the soup at the dinner lady. The next day the head master said "Since it is a snowy day all you children can shovel all the snow away from the school door. He gave them all a spade and they started to clear the snow. After a while their backs started to ache. When they had finished they said we will be good children all the time. The head master said "That is good".
(Alexa, aged 8)

Naughty, Naughty
Once a upon there was a school. All the children were naughty in this school. The teachers did not want to go to school. Then one day Mr Wilson the advisor came to school, he had a idea how to stop this. He told the teachers his idea. The next day the head teacher went to school happily. He told the children his idea and this is the idea. Today the teachers are going to be the children and the children are going to be the teachers. The teachers were running around wild. One of the children said that she was going to read a book but she did not know how to read. Then one of the children said we are going to sing a song but nobody could play the piano. When the cook came in the teachers were running around wild. The cook ran home as fast as she could. That day after the children were good for ever.
(Kim, aged 8)

Mr Murphy's Gnomes

The Gnome's Secret
One night I went to see my gnome sister. Her name was Sunlight. We had a party. We asked all the gnomes in the garden to come to

the party. We forgot where we stood in the garden. In the morning Mr Frimble knew our secret. He sold us so we could not see each other again. We escaped with our little tools. When Mr Frimble found out he stopped and he said "Gnomes, gnomes". And we went to our new home and we lived happily ever after.
(Kim, aged 8)

The day my house caught fire
One morning, when I was a gnome I went to visit Sleepy. Then I went to visit Mr Grumpty when I went home I made some tea. After I made some tea and I went to bed. In the morning when I got up I had some breakfast. Then I went to chop some wood. When I finished chopping the wood, I made a bonfire. I went to see Mr Sleepy and then I went to see Mr Grumpty. Then the bonfire went all over the place. when I went home there was a fire in my house. I went to Kims house because she had a telphone. I telphoned the fire engine and I went to live with Mr Grumpty. And we lived happily ever after.
(Scott, aged 8)

Fine Feathers

My Wish
One day I saw a pellican. It was a beautiful one. A fairy came to my nest. She gave me one wish. I said I saw a beautiful bird today. It was a pellican. I wish I was a pellican. I was a pellican the next morning. I was too big for my nest. I went down to the river to get my dinner. I have fish every day. When I went to my nest my leg's were too long. In the winter we went to another country where it was warmer. I was so sad. I wanted to be a robin again. The fairy came back so that I could be changed back into a robin.
(Kim, aged 8)

The Teddy Bears' Picnic

At Night
One night I thought I heard a noise. I heard it again. I got up and went down stairs. Then I saw scared. But I still went down stairs. I thought it was robber. I went to the sitting room, I got a blanket. I tried to go to sleep. but I could not. The wind banged on the window. I heard the noise again. It was like a tapping noise. I was to scared to switch on the light. I went to the kitchen. The noise

was louder. Then I saw a little man. I was scared. The man said why are you scared of me I am a friend. Will you be my friend? I said yes then I went to bed. The wind stopped and the noise stopped. I was able to get to sleep.
(*Lynn, aged 7*)

At Night
On Sunday night I heard a noise downstairs. I woke Scott up. He said shut up. I went downstairs by my self. I was scared. I went back upstairs. I woke Sean. He went down with me. Sean ran up and went back to sleep so I went down by myself. I opened the door and there was Santa filling the stockings up. I said to Santa do you want a piece of cake and a drink. Santa and I were laughing. Then it was morning I ran up stairs and pretended I was asleep when I woke up I was laughing. I said because I saw Santa. Scott said you are just pretending.
(*Craig, aged 8*)

The Robber
One night when it was late. I heard something downstairs. I did not know what it was. So I went downstairs to see what it was. I went to the livingroom door to see what it was. In the livingroom I saw a robber taking all our money away so I went to the phone and I dialed 999 for the police and I gave the my address. Then the police came and took the robber to jail. Before the robber went to jail he got all the money out of his pockets. Then the police gave all the money back to the people in the village and us.
(*Caroline, aged 8*)

That night
One night I went to bed and heard something downstairs. I thought I heard a noise. I went downstairs and then I stopped. The noise got louder. The noise was like a bear. So I went down and got dads gun. The wind was whistling. I switched on the light. I saw nothing. It went quiet. But I thought it was not a bear. someone was eating. I thought it was Becky, it could be the cats. I went into the room and there were the two cats, Becky, mam and dad with Elizabeth.
(*Nicola, aged 7*)

A sleepless night
One night I could not get to sleep. I thought I heard a noise

downstairs. I listened again. I was afraid. I went to get Dad. He said don't be stupid. Then Dad hard a sound. We both went downstairs. The sound was coming from out side. We went out side. It was Ross he was crying because we had locked him outside. We gave him something to eat and put him to bed. Then I was not afraid any more. I got to sleep.

(*Kim, aged 8*)

The Three Monsters

Robin Hood

I lived in Sherwood Forest, near Nottingham. With Little John and Friar Tuck, we hated the sheriff of Nottingham. We robbed all of the rich people when they past by and we give the money the poor people. All off the poor loved us and lots of them lived in Sherwood Forest. The sheriff of Nottingham looked over sherwood forst for us. If we got caught killing the king's dear we would be killed. I lived in Sherwood Forest for twenty two years. Then I became ill, I could not eat nor drink and I no longer cared for the things I used to love. I went to the priory. I give the prioress twenty pounds in good. I said to Friar Tuck were ever the arww lands threr will be my grave and pleaes buriey me with my boow and arwwre so I loosnd the last arrow from the string, and the I died. And where the arrow fell, I was buried.

(*Craig, aged 8*)

Scott

My name was Robert Falcon Scott. I was born in (1868–1912). I was an Navy officer and I was chosen to lead the 1910 Expedition which sailed in the Terra Nova.

In reached the Pole on January 17th 1912 only to find that Amandsen had just beaten me.

On the way back we met snow storms and blizzards. Evans and Oates died on the march and following spring a search party fond the bodies of the other three only 11 miles from safety. My diary shows that we kept our courage and cheerfulness to the end.

(*Scott, aged 8*)

Christopher Columbus

I was born in Italy about 1450. I went to sea when I was a boy and I learnt to make maps. I believed there was a shorter way than going

from Portugal all the way round Africa to India by going to the west. And I wished to prove it. I was promised help by King ferdinand and Queen Isabella of Spain. I sailed from Spain in 1492. The ship was called Sante Maria, it was a small ship and there was only 100 tons that carried 52 men, with two more small ships they were the pinta it had 50 tons and the Nina which had 40 tons. I sailed by the Canary Islands. I left there on the 6th September. After 30 whole days I was being forced by my crew to turn back in three more days. On the last day we set up the Royal Standard of Spain. We sailed on to Cuba, and then left some of the men on Haiti then we returned to Spain in the Nina. The Santa Maria had been wrecked in the Indies, and the Pinta lost on the way back. On the next voyage in 1493 I found some more islands. On my third voyage in 1498, I had discovered Trinidad and I discovered the South American main land. I also strengthened a colony I had left behind but my enemies at home set out a new governor. This governor sent me back to Spain as a prisoner in chains. I was set free in 1502 to make a fourth voyage, but this time I failed to find the passage to Asia for which I was seeking. I returned to Spain. It was such a disappointment. I was too sick to even to go to court, and in 1506 I died in poverty in the town of Valladolid.
(Alexa, aged 8)

Robert the Bruce

I was born in Scotland in 1274.

When I was grown-up I decided to carry on fighting the English. I escaped from the English court and fled to Scotland, where I expected to join my cousin Red Comyn. But I had a quarrell with my cousin and stabbed him to death in church. A handful of friends crowned me king of Scotland, but I was soon driven from one hiding-place to another by the English forces. I nearly gave up the fight. Because my brother was killed and my wife made prisoner. But more and more Scots came to my side, and by the time Edward I of England died, I had recaptured most of Scotland I next defeated an English army twice as large as my own, at the Battle of Bannockburn, and at last Edward II had to give up all hope of ruling over Scotland. So I ruled Scotland wisely from 1306 until my death from leprosy in 1329.
(Nicola, aged 7)

The Good Fairies

The Witch

One day a baby was born. It was my baby. Her name was Kim. At night three fairies were on my bed. They were lovingness, softnes and happiness. When the baby grew up she was happy, stoft and loving. Kim was playing a game with the dog. Then a wicked fairy came and said "You will lose you self in the big wood and never find you house again." A good fairy heard that but could not make the spell go away. One day Kim did lose her self in the wood. When her mother came to see her she said where is my baby. Her baby was still in the wood. One day a forester saw her and brought her back to her house.

(Lynn, aged 7)

The Baby

One day I went to see the newborn bady. She lived in the forest. I am the fairy of goodness. A big bird caught me. The bird was going to eat me for supper. But I escaped from his beak. But the bird chased me. I got away. I went into a cave for a rest. I saw a skeleton. I thought it was alive but I was glad it was not. Then I went to find my way to the house. I got to the house where the newborn baby lived and gave the bady a goodness. The bady's mother gave me something to eat. I said goodbye and went on my way.

(Kim, aged 8)

The Baby Fairy

When I was a fairy I was on my way to grant a wish to a baby. When I was nearly there I went into the house They I realised that I was in the wrong house. So when I was at the right house I went to give the baby some goodness so I went to see if he was good when he grew up. So when he was old I went to see him if his was good. He was good so he lived happily every after.

(Scott, aged 8)

The Wish That Came True

My wishes

One morning I went to work and I got back from work I wished and wished. when the moon was blue and the winds blowing down

The chimney. a fairy came into the bedroom and gave me three wishes. I wished that I could fly. I gave the other wishes to the next door neghboar. In the morning I got up and went to work. I jumped up into the sky and then I flew right into the clouds I was at work. *(Scott, aged 8)*

The Dream
One night a fairy came and said that I could have one wish. I thought and thought. Then I said I want to be a robin and fly all over the world. The next morning I was like a robin. I was a robin. I flew all over the bedroom and out of the window. I met some more birds. There were lots of sparrows and wrens. Then I found a tree. I made a nest on a branch and went to sleep. I had a dream. I dreamed that I was eating a fish. Then I woke up and saw a sparrow. I fell in love with her and married her. *(Lynn, aged 7)*

Troubled Wishes
One day there was a tap on the window. I opened it up and in flew a pink fairy. It was raining outside and she was soaked through. She asked she could dry herself by my fire. I said she could and she did. She said, "You were so kind that I will grant you a wish. I wished that I was a fairy that was pink with wings. Immediately I found myself flying around the room but I didn't look where I was going and I bumped into a door. I thought it was a good idea to not try it again. I walked on the floor but my legs were so fragile they broke. Suddenly, there was a flash of light and the fairy appeared again. I begged her to put me right and she did. She disappeared and I didn't even have time to say thankyou! *(Tracy, aged 9)*

What I wanted to be
One day I went for a walk. I saw something I thought I would like to be. It was a queen. I went to bed very sad because I was myself. Then when I woke up I saw a fly in my bedroom but it spoke. It said "I am a fairy and I give you one wish. You can be anyone anything." I said "I would like to be a queen." She said "I have had a lot of wishes to be a queen but just for you. You can be a queen." I jumped and screamed and she said "Queens do not do that." I said "Sorry." She gave me a crown and an ermine robe and she flew away. She said "Do not go out after nine o'clock at night." I said "OK". One day I forgot what the fariy said and I broke the wish and now I am very sad. *(Lorraine, aged 9)*

4 Ice goblins
hiding.

5 Father
Christmas and his
wife.

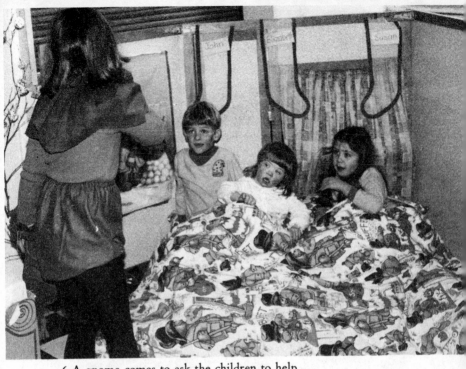

6 A gnome comes to ask the children to help.
7 Good triumphs over evil – the Ice goblins melt.

CHAPTER SEVEN

Cross-Reference of Resources and Publications

In this chapter I have tried to list other books and stories that can be used in connection with each story. The suggestions range from long stories to picture books for language development. To include every book would have been an impossible task, so I have tried to restrict them to books my own children have enjoyed and publications that have received favourable reports in the educational press.

The second half of the chapter includes a list of resources and information books for both the teacher and the children, to help back up the extended follow-up suggestions from Chapter Five.

The Cake That Made People Jump
Benny bakes a cake by Eve Rice (Bodley Head)
Mr Bear Baker Chizuko Kuratomi (Macdonald)
Shepherd's Pie Dorothy Clark (Julia MacRae Books)
The chicken scandal at Number Seven Rue Petit Ellen Shire (Hamish Hamilton)

Isabella's Oak
The past we see today Victor Neuberg (O.U.P.)
Jim and the beanstalk Raymond Briggs (Hamish Hamilton)

The Boy Who Couldn't Tell The Truth
Benjamin's dreadful dream Alan Baker (André Deutsch)
Lisa's lie Bernard Ashley (Julia MacRae Books)
Johnny's dragon Irina Korschunow, trans. Anthea Bell (Hippo)

The Children of Mulberry School
Mary Kate and the school bus Helen Morgan (Young Puffin)
Melanie Brown goes to school Pamela Oldfield (Faber Fanfare)
The Horrobilly goes to school M. Osborne and E. Brown (Heinemann)
Here comes the Horrobilly M. Osborne and E. Brown (Heinemann)
On my way to school Celia Berridge (André Deutsch)
Emma's first day at nursery school Gunilla Wolde (Hodder and Stoughton)
Emma enjoys nursery school Gunilla Wolde (Hodder and Stoughton)
My Brother Sean Petronella Breinburg and Errol Lloyd (Bodley Head)
I went to school one morning Guido Waldman (Bodley Head)
No school today F. Brandenburg and Aliki (Hamish Hamilton)
Blue Bell Hill games R.A. Smith and D. McKee (Kestrel)

The Chief of All the Chiefs
Myrtle Turtle Sheila Lavelle and Anni Axworthy (A. & C. Black)
Dorrie and the Screebit Ghost Patricia Coombs (World's Work)
Mister Magnolia Quentin Blake (Jonathon Cape)

Jeremy Jumbletop
The owl who was afraid of the dark Jill Tomlinson (Methuen)
Tom and Tina in Topsy-Turvey Town Colette Demez and Marie-José Sacré
  (Wheaton)

Monty Mean and Generous Jack
Mrs McGinty and the Bizarre Plant Gavin Bishop (O.U.P.)

The Lord Mayor's Clock
Clock and more clocks Pat Hutchins (Bodley Head)
Around the clock Judy Brook (World's Work)
What time is it when it isn't? Donald Bisset (Methuen)
Time Jan Pienkowski (Heinemann)
A first look at time Robin Kerrod (Franklin Watts)

Mr Tootle's Walking Stick
Is Milton missing? Steven Kroll (Warne)

The Princess Who Looked Down Her Nose
The King's flower Mitsumasa Anno (Bodley Head)
Mrs Fox's wedding Sara and Stephen Corrin (Faber)

The Terrible Traffic Jam
Paul the hero of the fire Edward Ardizzone (Kestrel)
Phoebe and the hot water bottles Terry Furchgott and Linda Dawson (André
  Deutsch)
How rabbit stole the fire Joanna Troughton (Blackie)
Arrow to the sun Gerald McDermott (Kestrel)
Crocodile's plaster Marjorie-Ann Watts (André Deutsch)
Crocodile medicine Marjorie-Ann Watts (André Deutsch)
Doctor Sean Petronella Breinburg and Errol Lloyd (Bodley Head)
Magic balloon, sleeping chair Helen Young and Hilary Abrahams (André
  Deutsch)
Monster goes to the hospital Ellen Blance and Ann Cook (Longman)
The *Thomas and Emma* series Gunilla Wolde (Hodder and Stoughton)
Topsy and Tim go to hospital Jean and Gareth Adamson (Blackie)
Topsy and Tim visit the dentist Jean and Gareth Adamson (Blackie)

The Man Who Mended Dolls
Little Spook and the lost doll Inger and Lasse Sandberg (Methuen)

Mr Murphy's Gnomes
Mr Plum's paradise Elisa Trimby (Faber)
Miss Jasper's garden N.M. Bodeker (Picture Lion)
My Aunt Polly Helen Cresswell (Wheaton)

The Teddy Minders
Bear hunt Anthony Browne (Hippo)

The Man Who Invented Nice Words
The happy helper engine Jill McDonald (Methuen)
Goldie the doll maker M.B. Goffstein (Canongate Publishing)

The Honky-Tonk Piano
Kassim's shoes Harold Berson (World's Work)

The Great Peanut Rush
The supermarket mystery Richard Scarry (Picture Lion)
Paddington goes shopping Michael Bond and Fred Banbury (Collins)

Marna's Paper Bag
Amelia Mouse and her great, great . . . granddaughter Ann van der Essen and
    Etienne Delessert (Evans)

Katinka, the Poor Princess
When Willy went to the wedding Judith Kerr (Collins)
The field of buttercups Alice Boden (Hamish Hamilton)
Gardener George goes to town Susan Moxley and Sara Sharp (Hodder and
    Stoughton)

Mrs Tippett and the Yellow Blanket
The wind blew Pat Hutchins (Picture Puffin)
Cath's Story Catherine Brighton (Evans)

Mrs Greenfinger
Nothing like a fresh coat of paint Peter Spier (World's Work)

Mr Brown and His Interesting Dog
The last puppy Frank Asch (Evans)
New dog next door Elizabeth Bridgeman (Hippo)

The Balloon Man
Bill's balloon ride Reiner Zimnik (Methuen)
Up and up Shirley Hughes (Bodley Head)
The boy and the bike Max Velthuijs (A. & C. Black)
The wonderful pumpkin Lennart Hellsing and Svend Otto (Pelham Books)

Father Christmas and the Ice Goblins
The snowman who went for a walk Winifred Opgenoorth (O.U.P.)
Christmas Ed. T.C.A. Goldsmith (Blandford)
The silver Christmas tree Pat Hutchins (Bodley Head)

Winter's tale Michael Foreman and Freire Wright (Benn)
The night before Christmas Clement Clark Moore and Elisa Trimby (Benn)
The big sneeze H.E. Todd and Val Biro (Hodder and Stoughton)
The cat of Dorrefell Tomie de Paola (Methuen)

Sam Snuffett
The trip Ezra Jack Keats (Hamish Hamilton)
The mouse and the winds Arnold Lobel ("I can read" series, World's Work)

The Princess and the Rainbow
The blue bird's shadow Peter Curry (World's Work)
Wet day witches Celia Berridge (André Deutsch)
A wet Monday Dorothy Edwards and Jenny Williams (Methuen)

Barney and the Easter Chicken
Cackler's egg Elizabeth Stiemart and Antonella Bolliger-Savelli (Dent)

The Silver Dollar
The treasure hunting trip Janosch, trans. Anthea Bell (Anderson Press)

Farmer John and the Night of the Terrible Storm
Farmer Brown and Guy Fawkes night John Cunliffe (André Deutsch)
The rainy day Eileen Ryder ("Headstart" series, Burke Books)
The great flood Peter Spier (World's Work)
Noah's Ark Judy Brook (World's Work)
Johnny Lion's rubber boots Edith Thacher Hurd ("I can read" series, World's Work)
The rain puddle Adelaid Hall and Roger Duvoisin (Bodley Head)
The rainy holiday Alice Boden (Hamish Hamilton)

Frogmorton
The tiny tiny tadpole H.E. Todd (Carousel)
I am a frog Keith Snow and Ferelith Eccles Williams (World's Work)
Frog and the watershrew Helen Piers and Pauline Baynes (Kestrel)

Ferdinand, Felipe and Fandango
Jump, frog, jump Byron Barton (Julia MacRae Books)
Life cycle of the frog Paula Hogan (Ward Lock)

The Special Friends
Operation hedgehog Margaret Lane and Patricia Casey (Methuen Walker)
I am a rabbit Keith Snow and Ferelith Eccles Williams (World's Work)
Hedgehog and puppy dog tales Ruth Manning Sanders (Methuen)
Oh really rabbit Ruth Manning Sanders (Methuen)
George and the buried treasure Robert Bright (World's Work)

The Beetle Who Lived in a Bottle
What-a-mess the good Frank Muir and Joseph Wright (Benn)
Grasshopper on the road Arnold Lobel (World's Work)

The Cat Who Stared
King of the cats Paul Galdone (World's Work)
Three by the sea Edward Marshall and James Marshall (Bodley Head)
Kittymouse Sumiko (Heinemann)

Fine Feathers
Chibby the little fish Gerda Marie Scheill (Dent)
Guy and the flowering plum tree Robin Stemp and Carolyn Dinan (Faber)
The seven sparrows and the motor car Joan Hickson (André Deutsch)
Flight of fancy Linda Allen and Gerald Rose (Abelard)
When the wind blows Linda Allen and Gerald Rose (Abelard)
Birds of a feather Linda Allen and Gerald Rose (Abelard)

The Teddy Bears' Picnic
Moonlight Jan Ormerod (Kestrel)
Teddy Bear, baker Phoebe and Selby Worthington (Warne)
Mr Bear, baker Chizuko Kuratomi and Kozo Kakimoto (Macdonald)
Bears bazaar Michael Cartlidge (Heinemann)

The Three Monsters
Zed and the monster Peggy Parrish and Paul Galdone (World's Work)
Amazing monsters Ed. Robert Fisher, ill. Rowena Allen (Faber)
Stanley: the tale of a lizard Peter Mateyard and Peter Firmin (André
   Deutsch)

The Terrible Scary Hairy Monster
King Krakus and the dragon Janina Domanska (Julia MacRae Books)
Where the wild things are Maurice Sendak (Bodley Head)

The Good Fairies
Ruth-Emma herself Karin Stjernholm Raeder, trans. Patricia Crampton
   (Kestrel)
The three magic gifts James Riordan and Errol le Cain (Kaye and Ward)

Margery Moonlight and the Magic Party
Benjamin's rocking horse Paula Geldenhuys (Macdonald and Jane's)
What happened at Rita's party? Petronella Breinburg (Kestrel)
Party pants William Mayne (Hodder and Stoughton)

Food From The Forest
Mushroom in the rain Mirra Ginsberg, Jose Aruego and Brian Dewey
   (Hamish Hamilton)

The Old Woman of The Woods

The magic pasta pot Tomie de Paola (Hutchinson)
Snow White and Rose Red James Reeves (Anderson Press)
The fisherman's son Mirra Ginsberg and Tony Chen (Julia MacRae Books)
Timothy and Gramps Ron Brooks (Collins)

A Long-Ago Story of the Mountain Pixies

My naughty little sister Dorothy Edwards (Young Puffin)
Long ago when the earth was flat Paola Luzzatto and Aimone Samburg (Collins)

The Wish That Came True

Too many husbands Sheila Lavelle and John Lawrence (Hamish Hamilton)
Wriggle the little wishing pig Pauline Watson and Paul Galdone (World's Work)

The Great Tug-of-War

Kidnap in Willowbank Wood Faith Jacques (Heinemann)
Professor Noah's spaceship Brian Wildsmith (O.U.P.)

Piko and the Growing-up Fairy

Magic growing powder Janet Quin-Harkin (Hamish Hamilton)
Thumbelina retold Amy Ehrlich, ill. Susan Jeffers (Hamish Hamilton)

The Amazing Washerwoman

The Mother Goose Book Alice and Martin Provensen (Julia MacRae Books)
Even Granny was young once Eva Janikovsky and I. Reba (Dobson Books)
Grandmother Lucy and her hats Joyce Wood and Frank Francis (Picture Lions)

The Wonderful Washing Machine

The magic pot Patricia Coombs (World's Work)
Rowbottom the robot Ian Fennell and David Higham (Methuen)

Story books to accompany seasons project

What-a-mess in Spring
What-a-mess in Summer
What-a-mess in Autumn
What-a-mess in Winter
Frank Muir and Joseph Wright (Benn)

Story books to reinforce the book

The ivory city Marcus Crouch (Pelham Books)
Once in a wood ill. Eve Rice (Bodley Head)

Poetry books to use with the book
Verse and various Charlotte Hough (Dent)
If you should meet a crocodile (World's Work)
Water, machines and toys Jean Gilbert (O.U.P.)
Selected cautionary verses Hilaire Belloc (Puffin)
Struwwelpeter (Piccolo Picture Book)
Collected poems and verses for children Leonard Clark (Dobson)
A child's garden of verse Robert Louis Stevenson (Puffin)
Peacock Pie Walter de la Mare (Faber Fanfare)
Tiggie Hobbin Charles Causley (Puffin)

Topics on food, diet and cooking (Group I of stories, page 235)
RESOURCES
Housecraft, published annually by the Association of Teachers of Domestic Science, gives details of materials and resources that can be obtained in Britain. Some of these materials are free and adaptable for use with younger children.
INFORMATION BOOKS
Cooking together Kay Preston (Macmillan Educational)
A first look at pots and pans L. Hinds (Franklin Watts)
I am a chef Dick Swayne (Dent)
Food, a resource for learning in the primary school (I.L.E.A.)
My learn to cook book Ursula Sedgewick (Hamlyn)
My fun to cook book Ursula Sedgewick (Hamlyn)
Cooking with mother (Ladybird)
Learnabout making and decorating a cake (Ladybird)
We can cook Lyn Peeples (Ladybird)
Floury Fingers Cecelina Hinde (Faber)
Sweets for presents Jenny Leggatt (Dinosaur)
First steps in cooking (Ward Lock)
Cooking is easy Jane Todd (Beaver)
Cookery Monique Felix (Busy Books)
Science 5–13 (Macdonald Educational)

Topics on light, rainbows, reflections (Group II of stories, page 237)
INFORMATION BOOKS
The magic mirror book Marion Walter (Scholastic Publications)
Another, another, another and more Marion Walter (André Deutsch)
What is symmetry? Mindel and Harry Sitomer (A.&C. Black)

Mirrors and magnifiers Dorothy Diamond (Macdonald Educational)
Nuffield Maths 2 Teachers' Handbook Monica Williams and Winifred Moore
    (Longman)
What do you know about mirrors? K.A. Shoesmith (Burke)
Light and colour ("First Library" series, Macdonad Educational)
Candles ("Teaching Primary Science" series, Macdonald Educational)
Making Light Marguerite Turnbull ("Read and Discover" series,
    Macdonald Educational)
Batteries and Bulbs ("Starters" series, Macdonald Educational)
Science 5–13 (Macdonald Educational)

Topics on my school, and playground culture (Group III of stories, page 240)

RESOURCES

"All Children Play", Fair Play for Children, 248 Kentish Town Road,
    London NW5 (cost about £2) – an information pack about games from
    Africa, China, India, Japan and the West Indies.
"Games Around the World", Publishing Department, UNICEF,
    46–48 Osnaburgh Street, London NW1 3PU (cost about £1.95) – a
    collection of 40 games, for both indoors and outdoors. The sheets also
    give an insight into life in the country of origin of each game.

INFORMATION BOOKS

Games children play around the world Susan Adams and Diana Holmes (John
    Adams Toys), available OXFAM Education Department (published
    for the Year of the Child)
Language teaching games W.R. Lee (O.U.P.)
Learning through play Jean Marzollo and Janice Lloyd (Penguin)
Let's play Asian children's games Opal Dunn (Macmillan)
One potato, two potato (A.&C. Black)
Play – its role in development and evolution Ed. J.S. Bruner, A. Jolly and
    K. Sylva (Penguin)
Talkabout starting school (Ladybird)
My nursery school Harlow Rockwell (Hamish Hamilton)
Starting school Althea (Dinosaur)
Janet at school P. White (A.&C. Black)
Berron's tooth Joan Soloman (Hamish Hamilton)
The teacher's handbook for environmental studies Perry, Jones and Hammersley
    (Blandford)
School in the town Barbara Blit (Evans)
Games André John and Monique Felix (Busy Books)

Topic on people who work for us
(Group IV of stories, page 243)

RESOURCES

The Fire Department, Home Office, 50 Queen Anne's Gate, London SW1

RoSPA, Cannon House, The Priory, Queensway, Birmingham

The Forestry Commission, Information Branch Schools, 231 Corstorphine Road, Edinburgh

The Slide Centre, 143 Chatham Road, London SW11

National Association for Welfare of Children in Hospital (NAWCH), 7 Exton Street, London SE1

Health Education Council, 78 New Oxford Street, London WC1

Eductional Productions Ltd, Bradford Road, East Ardsley, Wakefield, Yorkshire

National Water Council, Publications Dept, 1 Queen Anne's Gate, London SW1

You will find the addresses of the local Ambulance headquarters, Police Station and Water Authority in the telephone directory.

INFORMATION BOOKS

A first look at fire Dorothy Ralphs (Franklin Watts)

A first look at safety Daphne Gurton (Franklin Watts)

Come and see the fire station Julie Simpson (Longman)

Fighting fires Althea (Dinosaur)

Fighting fires Felicia Law ("Dandelion" series, Fontana)

Fires ("Basic Starters", Macdonald Educational)

Fire ("Leader" series, Ladybird)

Fire ("First Library" series, Macdonald Educational)

Fires and firemen H. Adams (Blackwell)

Fire engines in colour (Arthur Ingram and Denis Bishop (Blandford)

A first look at nurses Valerie Pitt (Franklin Watts)

All about me, Teachers' guide (Thomas Nelson)

Come and see the hospital Julie Simpson (Longman)

Going into hospital ⎤
Going to the doctor ⎥ Althea (Dinosaur)
Visiting the dentist ⎥
Having an eye test ⎦

Hospital Brian Ward ("Insiders" series, Macdonald Educational)

I go to hospital Althea (Souvenir Press)

Let's go to the doctor ⎤
Let's go to the dentist ⎥ Frank Peacock (Franklin Watts)
Let's go to the optician ⎦

My Doctor ⎤ Harlow Rockwell (Hamish Hamilton)
My Dentist ⎦

Paul in hospital Camilla Jessell (Methuen)

Something to say about feeling poorly Brian Ward (Evans)

Teeth ⎱ ("Starters" series, Macdonald Educational)
Hair ⎰

The ambulance man Richard Collingridge ("What to do" series, Macmillan Educational)

The nurse (Series 606B, Ladybird)

Your body ("Nature" series, Ladybird)

A first look at rain Philip Sauvain (Franklin Watts)

A first look at weather Robin Kerrod (Franklin Watts)

A young specialist looks at weather Siegfried Schöpfer (Burke Books)

The postman ("People at Work" series, Ladybird)

Rubbish Gerald Best and Robert Rowatt ("Man and His World" series, Blackie)

The Police   ⎫
The Post Office   ⎪
The Fire Service   ⎪
The Hospital   ⎬ Constance Milburn ("Inside Story" series, Blackie)
Airports   ⎪
Railways   ⎪
Waste disposal   ⎪
Water   ⎭

Topics on monsters, dinosaurs, mini-beasts (Group V of stories, page 245)

RESOURCES

The Slide Centre, 143 Chatham Road, London SW11

Educational Productions Ltd, Bradford Road, East Ardsley, Wakefield, Yorkshire

INFORMATION BOOKS

A companion of world mythology Richard Barber (Kestrel)

Abbey Lubbers, Banshees and Boggarts Katherine Briggs and Yvonne Gilbert (Kestrel)

Fabulous animals David Attenborough (BBC Publications)

Fabulous beasts Richard Blyth (Macdonald Educational)

Fabulous beasts Christopher Fagg (Piccolo Explorer)

Loch Ness monster Rosemary Border ("Mysteries" series, Macdonald Educational)

Monsters of the mountains Jon Jameson (Franklin Watts)

The Abominable Snowman Tyrus Huffman ("Mysteries" series, Macdonald Educational)

The amazing fact book of monsters (Franklin Watts)

The Loch Ness Monster E. Rabinowich (Franklin Watts)

Collins book of dinosaurs Tom McGowen (Collins)
Dinosaurs Richard Moody ("Insight" books, Hamlyn)
Dinosaurs ("Leader" series, Ladybird)
Dinosaurs and prehistoric animals (Ladybird)
Dinosaurs of the earth (Collins)
Dinosaurs Ed. Henry Pluckrose ("Small World" series, Hamish Hamilton)
Dinosaurs time Peggy Parrish and Arnold Lobel (World's Work)
Piccolo picture book of dinosaurs Beverley Halstead (Piccolo)
Brontosaurus, Stegosaurus, Triceratops, Tyranosaurus – a four book series by
    Angela Sheehan (Franklin Watts)
A new look at dinosaurs Alan Charig (Heinemann)
Mini-beasts ("Science 5–13" series, Macdonald Educational)
STORY BOOKS
A.B.C. of monsters Deborah Niland (Hodder and Stoughton)
A book of monsters Ruth Manning Sanders (Methuen)
Beauty and the Beast Rosemary Harris and Errol le Cain (Faber)
Desmond and the monster Althea (Dinosaur)
Fairytales of Gold Alan Garner and Michael Foreman (Collins)
Frankenstein's dog Jan Wahl and Kay Choras (Hutchinson)
Go away and stay away Gail Haley (Bodley Head)
I believe in unicorns Adam Munthe and Elizabeth Falconer (Chatto and
    Windus)
Now, now, Bernard David McKee (Anderson Press)
Seven little monsters Maurice Sendak (Bodley Head)
The Hobyah Simon Stern (Methuen)
The palace on the moon Ruzena Wood (André Deutsch)
The story of Prince Rama Brian Thompson and Jeroo Ray (Kestrel)
The terrible Nung Gwama Ed. Young (Collins)
Dragon fire Ann Ruffell ("Gazelle" series, Hamish Hamilton)
Charlie, Emma and the Dragon Family Margaret Greaves (Methuen)
Danny and the dinosaurs Syd Hoff (World's Work)
Desmond and the dinosaurs Althea (Dinosaur)
Dinosaurs and all that rubbish Michael Foreman (Picture Puffin)
Meg's Eggs Helen Nicholl and Jan Pienkowski (Picture Puffin)
Monster goes to the museum Ellen Blance and Alan Cook (Longman)
The village dinosaurs Phyllis Arkle (Young Puffin)
Green smoke Rosemary Manning (Puffin)
Dragon in danger Rosemary Manning (Puffin)
The dragon's quest Rosemary Manning (Puffin)
POETRY BOOKS
Dinosaurs and beasts of yore sel. William Cole (Collins)
Oh Dinosaur! Barbara Iveson and Ann Axworthy (Corgi Carousel)
Please tell me Pterodactyl Charles Connell (Beaver)

Topics on weather and the seasons
(Stories grouped in Chapter Two, page 94)

RESOURCES

The Kite and Balloon Co., 613 Garratt Lane, London SW18

The Kite Store, 69 Neal Street, London WC2

You will find the address of the local weather centre in the telephone directory.

INFORMATION BOOKS

Air ("First Library" series, Macdonald Educational)

Balloon ("Starters" series, Macdonald Educational)

Kites ("Starters" series, Macdonald Educational)

Air ("Leaders" series, Ladybird)

Air is all around you ("Let's read and find out" series, A.&C. Black)

Air, wind and flight (Series 621, Ladybird)

Kites to make and fly Jack Newnham (Practical Puffin)

A first look at winds Philip Sauvain (Franklin Watts)

A first look at kites and gliders J.P. Rutland (Franklin Watts)

Windpower Heinz Kurth (World's Work)

Something to say about the wind Bill Michael and Bill Moffatt (Evans)

A first look at rain Philip Sauvain (Franklin Watts)

A first look at weather Robin Kerrod (Franklin Watts)

A young specialist looks at the weather Siegfried Schöpfer (Burke Books)

Instant weather forecasting Alan Watts, (Adlard Coles)

Spotter's guide to the weather (Usborne)

The Weather ("Visual Books", Macdonald Educational)

Weather ("How and Why" series, Transworld)

Weather ("New Reference Library", Macdonald Educational)

Weather ("First Library" series, Macdonald Educational)

Weather and Life Alan Hammersley (Blandford)

Weather, questions answered J. Merrigan (Hart-Davis)

Animals that sleep in winter Dr Gwynne Vener and Colin Treadgall (Bodley Head)

Animals in winter Venessa Luff (A.&C. Black)

Finding out about things outdoors Elliott Humberstone (Usborne)

Hot and cold Peggy Blakely (A.&C. Black)

Hot and cold ("Starters Science" series, Macdonald Educational)

Snow and ice Philip Sauvain (Franklin Watts)

Snow Lesley Ann ("Headstart" series, Burke)

Snow ("Basic Starters" series, Macdonald Educational)

Weather watch Adam Ford (Methuen)

Winter Richard Allington and Kathleen Krull, ill. John Wallner (Blackwell/Raintree)

Woodland in autumn and winter Jean Imrie (A.&C. Black)

CHAPTER EIGHT

Some Suggestions of Music to Use with the Stories

I have tried to compile a list of hymns, songs and pieces of music that can be used in connection with the stories. I admit that I am not a musical person, so I have relied heavily on *Alleluya, Someone's singing, Lord, Okko-tokki-unga, Apusskidu* and the other excellent music books published by A.&C. Black Ltd. I have included some songs from back copies of the *Child Education* magazine published by Scholastic Publications (Magazines) Limited.

I called upon the music advisor for the Northumberland Education Authority, Mr John Hollingworth, to assist me with this chapter. I am indebted to him for providing me with a comprehensive list of pieces of music that can be used under a range of topic headings.

The Cake That Made People Jump
Someone's Singing, Lord (A.&C. Black)
"Lord, I love to stamp and shout"
"For all the strength we have"
"Hands to work and feet to run"
"I danced in the morning"
"When the corn is planted"
Okki-Tokki-Unga (A.&C. Black)
"Eat brown bread"
"Someone's in the kitchen with Dinah"
"Ten fat sausages"
"I jump out of bed in the morning"
"Have you any bread and wine?"
Apusskidu (A.&C. Black)
"The super-supper march"
Child Education January 1979
"The runaway pancake" by Elizabeth Bennett
This Little Puffin (Puffin)
"Five currant buns"
Child Education Special Number 12
"Two in the middle and you can't jump" by Diana Thompson

Isabella's Oak
Someone's singing, Lord (A.&C. Black)
"This is a lovely world"
"To God who makes all lovely things"
"Over the earth is a mat of green"
"Who's that sitting in the sycamore tree?"
Okki-Tokki-Unga (A.&C. Black)
"The wild oak tree"
"Neath the spreading chestnut tree"
"Ten little squirrels"
Child Education Special Number 19 (1981)

"The oak tree" by David Dyke

The Boy who Couldn't Tell The Truth
Alleluya (A.&C. Black)
"This train is bound for glory"
Someone's singing, Lord (A.&C. Black)
"Father, we thank you for the night"
Okki-Tokki-Unga (A.&C. Black)
"Neath the lilacs"
"Let's all play Indians"
"Nicky, knacky, knocky, noo"
This Little Puffin (Puffin)
"I went to school one morning"

The Children of Mulberry School
Alleluya (A.&C. Black)
"The games people play"
"Children go, I will send you"
Someone's singing, Lord (A.&C. Black)
"Hands to work and feet to run"
"At half past three we go home to tea"
"We're going home"
Okki-Tokki-Unga (A.&C. Black)
"Join in the game"
"This way, that-a way"
"Let's all play at Indians"
"Nicky, knacky, knocky, noo"
Apusskidu (A.&C. Black)
"Shoot, shoot, shoot"
"One potato, two potato"
Song Games from Trinidad and Tobago J.D. Elder (Soma Books)
This Little Puffin (Puffin)
"I went to school one morning"

The Chief of All the Chiefs
Alleluya (A. & C. Black)
"Last night I had the strangest dream"
"Peace will soon come to be"
"You've got to walk that lonesome valley"
"Shalōm"
Okki-Tokki-Unga (A. & C. Black)
"Looby Loo"
"Okki-Tokki-Unga"
"One elephant"
Apusskidu (A. & C. Black)
"I whistle a happy tune"
"Apusski dusky"
The Turtle Drum by Malcolm Arnold and Ian Serraillier (O.U.P.)
"Divertissement of the deep"

Jeremy Jumbletop
Someone's singing, Lord (A. & C. Black)
"Father, we thank you for the night"
"Can you count the stars?"
"When lamps are lighted in the town"
Okki-Tokki-Unga (A. & C. Black)
"The galloping major"
"Did you ever see a lassie?"
Apusskidu (A. & C. Black)
"When father papered the parlour"
Child Education March 1983
"You're smiling"

Monty Mean and Generous Jack
Alleluya (A. & C. Black)
"Last night I had the strangest dream"
"Peace will soon come to be"
"You've got to walk that lonesome valley"
Okki-Tokki-Unga (A. & C. Black)
"Loobo Loo"
"Okki-tokki-unga"
"One elephant"
Apusskidu (A. & C. Black)
"I whistle a happy tune"
"Apusski dusky"
Child Education May 1981
"Building up my house" by Peter Charlton

The Lord Mayor's Clock
Alleluya (A. & C. Black)
"Lullaby for the times"
Someone's singing, Lord (A. & C. Black)
"Hands to work and feet to run"
"We have a king who rides a donkey"
Child Education January 1981
"My grandfather's clock"

Mr Tootle's Walking Stick
Alleluya (A. & C. Black)
"Music of the world a-turning"
Someone's singing, Lord (A. & C. Black)
"Come let us remember the joys of the town"
"Hands to work and feet to run"
Child Education May 1981
"Building up my house" by Peter Charlton
Sing-a-Song One (Nelson/ILEA)
"Round and round the village"
Singing Fun (Harrap)
"Ten miles from home"

The Princess Who Looked Down Her Nose
Someone's singing, Lord (A. & C. Black)
"To God who makes all lovely things"
"The sun that shines across the sea"
"The flowers that grow in the garden"
Okki-Tokki-Unga (A. & C. Black)
"The princess"
Child Education Special Number 17 (1981)
"I looked in the mirror and looked at my nose", words by Aileen Fisher from *The Young Puffin Book of Verse* (Puffin)

The Terrible Traffic Jam
Alleluya (A. & C. Black)
"Bus story"
"Moving on song"
Someone's singing, Lord (A. & C. Black)
"Come, let us remember the joys of the town"
Okki-Tokki-Unga (A. & C. Black)

"The wheels on the bus"
"The galloping major"
Apusskidu (A.&C. Black)
"Wheels keep turning"
"The fireman"
Words and Music (BBC Music Time)
  (BBC Publications)
"There are sounds all around"
Child Education May 1981
"Building up my house" by Peter
  Charlton

The Man Who Mended Dolls
Someone's singing, Lord (A.&C. Black)
"Hands to work and feet to run"
"Look out for loneliness"
"Think, think on these things"
Okki-Tokki-Unga (A.&C. Black)
"Miss Polly"
"The three bears"

Mr Murphy's Gnomes
Alleluya (A.&C. Black)
"Where have all the flowers gone?"
Someone's singing, Lord (A.&C. Black)
"Think of a world without any
  flowers"
"When I needed a neighbour"
"All the flowers are waking"
"The flowers that grow in the
  garden"
Okki-Tokki-Unga (A.&C. Black)
"The wise man and the foolish
  man"

The Teddy Minders
Okki-Tokki-Unga (A.&C. Black)
"Miss Polly"
"The three bears"
Apusskidu (A.&C. Black)
"The bear went over the mountain"

**The Man Who Invented Nice
  Words**
Alleluya (A.&C. Black)
"Let there be peace on earth"
"Make me a channel of your peace"
"Last night I had the strangest dream"
"Peace will soon come to be"

"A better world"
"Shalōm"
Someone's singing, Lord (A.&C. Black)
"To God who makes all lovely things"
Okki-Tokki-Unga (A.&C. Black)
"The wise man and the foolish man"
Apusskidu (A.&C. Black)
"Michael Finnigan"
"Down in Demerara"
"Apusski dusky"
From *Mary Poppins*
"Supercalafragelisticexpialidoceous"

The Honky-Tonk Piano
Someone's singing, Lord (A.&C. Black)
"Hands to work and feet to run"
Okki-Tokki-Unga (A.&C. Black)
"The music man"
"Oh! We can play the big bass
  drum"

The Great Peanut Rush
Someone's singing, Lord (A.&C. Black)
"Come, let us remember the joys of
  the town"
Okki-Tokki-Unga (A.&C. Black)
"A-tisket, a-tasket"
"The no laugh race"
Apusskidu (A.&C. Black)
"Bananas in pyjamas"
Sing-a-Song One (Nelson/ILEA)
"Round and round the village"
Singing Fun (Harrap)
"Ten miles from home"
Child Education May 1981
"Building up my house" by Peter
  Charlton

Marna's Paper Bag
Alleluya (A.&C. Black)
"Streets of London"
Someone's singing, Lord (A.&C. Black)
"Come, let us remember the joys of
  the town"
"Milk bottle tops and paper bags"
Apusskidu (A.&C. Black)
"The Wombling Song"
Sing-a-Song One (Nelson/ILEA)
"Round and round the village"

Child Education Special Number 12
"Floating down the river" by Diana
Thompson

Katinka, the Poor Princess
Someone's singing, Lord (A. & C. Black)
See under "The Princess Who
Looked Down Her Nose"
Okki-Tokki-Unga (A. & C. Black)
"The princess"
Seventy Simple Songs with Ostanati by
Albert Chatterly (Novello)
"Oh won't you buy my blooming
lavender"
Our Chalet Song Book (Halston)
"In nearby woods are sweet-
smelling violets"
Things that Help Us by Edward
Hughes (Novello)
"Flowers"
New Horizon by June Tillman
(Galliards)
"Summer, summer time"
"Water in the rain"
"Birds in the sky"
*Music in Action: The Sound of the
Country* by William Bullman
(Hart-Davis)
"Country garden"
The Lollipop Man by Cynthia Raza
(Stainer and Bell)
"Summer, summer"
Playschool Ideas by Ruth Croft (BBC
Publications)
Musical Fun with the Brownie Pack
(The Girl Guide Association)
"I like flowers"

**Mrs Tippett and the Yellow
Blanket**
Someone's singing, Lord (A. & C. Black)
"Hands to work and feet to run"
"Look out for loneliness"
"Think, think on these things"
Okki-Tokki-Unga (A. & C. Black)
"A-tisket, a-tasket"
Apusskidu (A. & C. Black)
"Yellow submarine"

Mrs Greenfinger
Alleluya (A. & C. Black)
"A rose is sweet"
"The fields are white"
Someone's singing, Lord (A. & C. Black)
"I have seen the golden sunshine"
"To God, who makes all lovely
things"
"Over the earth is a mat of green"
"Think of a world without any
flowers"
*Music in Action: The Sound of the
Country* by William Bullman
(Hart-Davis)
"Country Garden"
The Land of Wrong Way Round by
Christopher Row (Stainer and
Bell)
"The seed song"
Child Education September 1979
"The harvest festival" by Dave and
Toni Arthur
Child Education Special Number 13
(1980)
"Harvest" by Wendy Bird
Child Education March 1980
"Spring" by Gill Daniell

**Mr Brown and His Interesting
Dog**
Alleluya (A. & C. Black)
"Rain and sun"
"Blowing in the wind"
Someone's singing, Lord (A. & C. Black)
"I have seen the golden sunshine"
"Who can see the great wind?"
Apusskidu (A. & C. Black)
"I know an old lady"
"Where, oh where has my little dog
gone?"
"Daddy wouldn't buy me a bow-wow"

The Balloon Man
"Let's go fly a kite" words and
music by Richard M. Sherman and
Robert B. Sherman (Wonderful
Music Co. Inc.)
Someone's singing, Lord (A. & C. Black)
"Think, think on these things"

Father Christmas and the Ice Goblins

Carol Gaily Carol (A. & C. Black)
Merrily to Bethlehem (A. & C. Black)
These two books provide a wealth of Christmas carols and songs that are both unusual and popular.
Knock at the Door by Jan Betts (Ward Lock)
"The North Wind doth blow"
"Who saw footprints in the snow?"
BBC Music Time Autumn 1977
"Jesus birthday carol" words Brian Kenny, music Bruce Cole
"Travelling" words Brian Kenny, music Bruce Cole
Someone's singing, Lord (A. & C. Black)
"Look for signs that Summer's done"
"See how the snowflakes are falling"

Sam Snuffett

Alleluya (A. & C. Black)
"Rain and sun"
"Raindrops keep falling"
Someone's singing, Lord (A. & C. Black)
"I have seen the golden sunshine"
Apusskidu (A. & C. Black)
"The wind blow east"
Knock at the Door by Jan Betts (Ward Lock)
"The north wind doth blow"
"Who saw footprints in the snow?"

The Princess and the Rainbow

Someone's singing, Lord (A. & C. Black)
"To God, who makes all lovely things"
"This is a lovely world"
Okki-Tokki-Unga (A. & C. Black)
"The princess"
Apusskidu (A. & C. Black)
"Sing a rainbow"
New Horizon by June Tillman (Galliards)
"Water in the sky"

Barney and the Easter Chicken

Someone's singing, Lord (A. & C. Black)
"The Golden Cockerel"
"I have seen the golden sunshine"
"Give us eyes to see"
"He gave me eyes so I could see"
Child Education March 1980
"Spring" by Gill Daniell
"Easter eggs" by Gill Daniell

The Silver Dollar

Alleluya (A. & C. Black)
"Magic Penny"
"Silver Trumpet"
Child Education March 1983
"You're smiling"
Child Education Special Number 17 (1981)
"I looked in the mirror and looked at my nose" words by Aileen Fisher from *The Young Puffin Book of Verse* (Puffin)
Child Education December 1979
"When the light goes out" by Elizabeth Bennett

Farmer John and the Night of the Terrible Storm

Alleluya (A. & C. Black)
"What have they done to the rain?"
"Someone got lost in a storm"
"Raindrops keep fallin' on my head"
"Moses, I know you're the man"
"Rise and shine"
Someone's singing, Lord (A. & C. Black)
"Who built the Ark"
"The farmer comes to scatter the seed"
Apusskidu (A. & C. Black)
"Song of the Delhi Tongawal lah"
"Animals went in two by two"
"Ferdinando, the donkey"
New Horizon by June Tillman (Galliards)
"Water in the sky"
The Nursery Song, A Picture Book by Winifred Barward (Wheaton)
"Pitter, patter"

Music

Frogmorton
Someone's singing, Lord (A.&C. Black)
"I have seen the golden sunshine"
"This is a lovely world"
"To God who makes all lovely
  things"
Okki-Tokki-Unga (A.&C. Black)
"Six little ducks"
Apusskidu (A.&C. Black)
"Five little frogs"
"Frog went a-courtin'"
Singing Fun (Harrap)
"Ten little speckled frogs"

Ferdinand, Felipe and Fandango
Someone's singing, Lord (A.&C. Black)
"This is a lovely world"
"To God who made all lovely things"
"When I needed a neighbour"
Okki-Tokki-Unga (A.&C. Black)
"Six little ducks"
Apusskidu (A.&C. Black)
"Five little frogs"
"Frog went a-courtin'"
Singing Fun (Harrap)
"Ten little speckled frogs"

The Special Friends
Alleluya (A.&C. Black)
"With a little help from my friends"
Someone's singing, Lord (A.&C. Black)
"When I needed a neighbour"
"This is a lovely world"
"To God who makes all lovely things"
"Can you count the stars?"
"When lamps are lighted in the town"
Okki-Tokki-Unga (A.&C. Black)
"Do your ears hang low?"
Apusskidu (A.&C. Black)
"Rabbit ain't got"
"A windmill in old Amsterdam"
"Risha, Rasha, Rusha"
Child Education March 1983
"You're smiling"

The Beetle Who Lived in a Bottle
Alleluya (A.&C. Black)
"Little boxes"
Someone's singing, Lord (A.&C. Black)

"When I needed a neighbour"
Okki-Tokki-Unga (A.&C. Black)
"The miner's dream of a home"
"The ants go marching"
Apusskidu (A.&C. Black)
"Little brown jug"
Child Education May 1981
"Building up my house" by Peter
  Charlton

The Cat Who Stared
Someone's singing, Lord (A.&C. Black)
"Give to us eyes"
"He gave me eyes so I could see"
"We have a king who rides a donkey"
Apusskidu (A.&C. Black)
"Gobbolino, the witch's cat"
"I know an old lady"

Fine Feathers
Someone's singing, Lord (A.&C. Black)
"The Golden Cockerell"
"This is a lovely world"
"To God who makes all lovely things"
"A little tiny bird"
"All things which live beneath the
  sky"
"Little birds in winter time"
Okki-Tokki-Unga (A.&C. Black)
"Six little ducks"
Apusskidu (A.&C. Black)
"Sparrow twitter"
"I know an old lady"
"The Ugly Duckling" (From the
  film about Hans Christian
  Andersen)

The Teddy Bears' Picnic
Someone's singing, Lord (A.&C. Black)
"Father, we thank you for the
  night"
"I have seen the golden sunshine"
"Can you count the stars?"
"When lamps are lighted in the town"
"When I needed a neighbour"
Okki-Tokki-Unga (A.&C. Black)
"The three bears"
Apusskidu (A.&C. Black)
"The super-supper march"

"The bear went over the mountain"
"The Teddy Bears' Picnic" (recorded by many artistes)

The Three Monsters
Someone's singing, Lord (A.&C. Black)
"When a knight won his spurs"
Okki-Tokki-Unga (A.&C. Black)
"Do your ears hang low?"
"The prehistoric animal brigade"
Apusskidu (A.&C. Black)
"The hippopotamus song"
"The elephant"
"Maggon, the bad tempered dragon"
Chorus: The Puffin Colony Song Book (Puffin)
"If you cross a mouse"

The Terrible Scary Hairy Monster
Someone's singing, Lord (A.&C. Black)
"Look out for loneliness"
"I love God's tiny creatures"
Okki-Tokki-Unga (A.&C. Black)
"The prehistoric animal brigade"
"The animal fair"
"Do your ears hang low?"
"One elephant"
Apusskidu (A.&C. Black)
"The hippopotamus song"
"The elephant"
"Maggon, the bad tempered dragon"
The Turtle Drum by Malcolm Arnold and Ian Serraillier (O.U.P.)
"Divertissement of the deep"
Child Education June 1981
"Land of the Monsters" by Jean Gilbert
Child Education Special Number 10 (1980)
"The Big Beasts Boogle" by Leonora Davies
Child Education February 1983
"Wild and Wary" by David Moses

The Good Fairies
Someone's singing, Lord (A.&C. Black)
"I have seen the golden sunshine"
"This is a lovely world"
"To God who makes all lovely things"

Okki-Tokki-Unga (A.&C. Black)
"In a cottage in a wood"

Margery Moonlight and the Magic Party
Someone's singing, Lord (A.&C. Black)
"Father, we thank you for the night"
"I have seen the golden sunshine"
Apusskidu (A.&C. Black)
"Old woman, old woman"
"There was an old witch"
"Gobbolino, the witch's cat"
Child Education October 1980
"Five old witches" by Elizabeth Bennett

Food From The Forest
Alleluya (A.&C. Black)
"Agada"
Someone's singing, Lord (A.&C. Black)
"I have seen the golden sunshine"
"Over the earth is a mat of green"
Okki-Tokki-Unga (A.&C. Black)
"'Neath the spreading chestnut tree"
"In a cottage in a wood"
"Ten little squirrels"
Our Chalet Song Book (Halston)
"In nearby woods are sweet-smelling violets"

The Old Woman of The Woods
Alleluya (A.&C. Black)
"Agada"
Someone's singing, Lord (A.&C. Black)
"Over the earth is a mat of green"
Okki-Tokki-Unga (A.&C. Black)
"'Neath the spreading chestnut tree"
"In a cottage in a wood"
"Ten little squirrels"
"There was an old witch"
Apusskidu (A.&C. Black)
"Old woman, old woman"
"Gobbolino, the witch's cat"
Child Education October 1980
"Five old witches" by Elizabeth Bennett

A Long-Ago Story of the Mountain Pixies
Alleluya (A. & C. Black)
"Abundantly"
"Kol dōdi"
"Temptation"
Someone's singing, Lord (A. & C. Black)
"Father, we thank you for the night"
Apusskidu (A. & C. Black)
"She'll be coming round the mountains"

The Wish That Came True
Okki-Tokki-Unga (A. & C. Black)
"Head, shoulders, knees and toes"
"I'm a little teapot"
"John Brown's baby"
"Sally Saucer"
Apusskidu (A. & C. Black)
"Li'l Liza Jane"
"The clown"

The Great Tug-of-War
Alleluya (A. & C. Black)
"Last night I had the strangest dream"
"Peace will soon come to be"
"Peace is flowing like a river"
"Hevenu Shalōm"
"A better world"
"Oh! the Lord looked"
Someone's singing, Lord (A. & C. Black)
"For all the strength we have"

Okki-Tokki-Unga (A. & C. Black)
"The wise man and the foolish man"
"The no laugh race"
Child Education October 1980
"Five old witches" by Elizabeth Bennett

Piko and the Growing-up Fairy
Okki-Tokki-Unga (A. & C. Black)
"Head, shoulders, knees and toes"
"I'm a little teapot"
"John Brown's baby"
"Sally Saucer"
Apusskidu (A. & C. Black)
"Li'l-Liza Jane"

The Amazing Washerwoman
Someone's singing, Lord (A. & C. Black)
"Hands to work and feet to run"
Okki-Tokki-Unga (A. & C. Black)
"In a cottage in a wood"
"There was an old witch"
Child Education October 1980
"Five old witches" by Elizabeth Bennett

The Wonderful Washing Machine
Someone's singing, Lord (A. & C. Black)
"When I needed a neighbour"
Apusskidu (A. & C. Black)
"When father papered the parlour"

Pieces of music, grouped by topic

ANIMALS
Bach *Cantata No. 208* ("Sheep May Safely Graze")
Britten *Noyes Fludd*
Coates *The Three Bears*
Elgar *Wand of Youth Suite* No. 2 ("March", "The Little Bells", "Moths and Butterflies", "Fountain Dance", "The Tame Bears", "The Wild Bears")
Fauré *Dolly Suite* Op. 56
Haydn *Symphony No. 82* (*The Bear*)

Ibert *The Little White Donkey* (*Le petit âne blanc*)
Mussorgsky *Pictures from an Exhibition* ("The Gnome", "The Old Castle", "Tuilleries", "Ox Cart", "Unhatched Chicks Ballet", "Two Polish Jews", "Market Place at Limoges", "Catacombs", "Baba jaga", "Great Gate of Kiev")
Prokofiev *Peter and the Wolf*
Saint-Saens *Carnival of the Animals* ("Royal March of the Lion",

"Cocks and Hens", "Wild Asses",
"Tortoises", "Elephant", "Kanga-
roos", "Aquarium", "People with
long ears", "Cuckoo", "Aviary",
"Pianists", "Swan", "Finale")

BIRDS

Beethoven *Symphony No. 6 in F*
   (*Pastoral*)
Coates *By the Sleepy Lagoon* ("Desert
   Island Discs")
Daquin *The Cuckoo*
Delius *Late Swallows*
Delius *On Hearing the First Cuckoo in
   Spring*
Harty *With the Wild Geese*
Messiaen *Oiseaux exotiques for piano
   and small orchestra*
Messiaen *Réveil des Oiseaux*
Mussorgsky *Pictures from an
   Exhibition* ("Unhatched Chicks
   Ballet")
Respighi *The Birds*
Rossini *The Thieving Magpie*
Saint-Saens *Carnival of the Animals*
   ("Cocks and Hens", "Cuckoo",
   "Aviary", "Swan")
Sibelius *The Swan of Tuonela* from
   Legends Op. 22
Smetana *The Little Hen* from *Czech
   Dances* No. 2
Stravinsky *Song of the Nightingale*
   (symphonic poem)
Stravinsky *The Firebird* (ballet)
Vaughan Williams *The Lark Ascending*

CIRCUS

Albeniz *Carnival in Seville*
Berlioz *Roman Carnival* Overture
Leoncavallo *I Pagliacci* Opera
Smetana *The Bartered Bride*
Stravinsky *Circus Polka*
Gilbert Vinter *Lisbon Carnival*

DAWN

Delius *Song Before Sunrise*
Elgar *Chanson de Matin*
Grieg *Peer Gynt* suite
Grofé *Grand Canyon Suite*

FAIRIES

Malcolm Arnold *Tam O'Shanter*
Berlioz *Symphonie Fantastique*
Eric Coates *Wood Nymphs*
Dukas *La Peri – poème danse*
Grieg *In the Hall of the Mountain King*
   from *Peer Gynt*
Humperdinck *Hansel and Gretel*
Mendelssohn *A Midsummer Night's
   Dream*
Ravel *Mother Goose* suite – "The
   Fairy Garden"
Saint-Saens *Danse Macabre* Op. 40
Sibelius *Legends* Op. 22
Wagner *The Flying Dutchman*
Weber *Oberon Overture*

FAIRS AND MARKETS IN
CITIES

Berlioz *Roman Carnival*
Coates *London suite*
Delius *Brigg Fair*
Dvorak *Carnival* Overture
Elgar *Cockaigne* Overture ("London
   Town")
Grainger *Mock Morris*
Grainger *Shepherd's Hey*
Ireland *London suite*
Khachaturian *Waltz* from *Masquerade*
Ravel *Rhapsodie Espagnole*
Respighi *Roman Festival*
Tschaikowsky *Capriccio Italien*

FIRE

Debussy *Feux d'Artifice* from Prelude
   Book 2 Number 24
Manuel de Falla *Ritual Fire Dance*
Handel *Music for Royal Fireworks*
Holst *The Perfect Fool*
Stravinsky *Fireworks Fantasy* Op. 4
Stravinsky *The Firebird* (ballet)

FISH

Bizet *The Pearl Fishers*
Debussy *Poissons d'Or* from *Images*
   Set 2, No. 3

GYPSIES

Albeniz *Iberia*

Bizet *Carmen*
Bizet *The Fair Maids of Perth*
Borodin *Polovlsian Dances* from *Prince Igor*
Brahms *Hungarian Dances*
Grieg *Norwegian Dances*
Liszt *Hungarian Rhapsodies*
Rimsky-Korsakov *Capriccio Espagnol* Op. 34
Johann Strauss *The Gypsy Baron*

INSECTS
Herb Alpert *Spanish Flea*
Grieg *Butterfly* from *Lyric Pieces* Op. 47
Mussorgsky *Song of the Flea*
Rimsky-Korsakov *Flight of the Bumblebee*
Roussel *Spider's Banquet*
Vaughan Williams Overture from *The Wasps*

NIGHT/DARKNESS
Elgar *Chanson de Nuit* Op. 15
Mussorgsky *Night on the Bare Mountain*
Offenbach *Orpheus in the Underworld*

TOYS
Debussy *Children's Corner* suite
Delibes *Coppelia*
Dohnanyi *Variations on a Nursery Song*
Elgar *The Nursery Suite*
Falla *Master Peter's Puppet Show*
Faure *The Dolly Suite*
Pierne *March of the Little Toy Soldiers*
Rossini *La Boutique Fantasque*
Schumann *Scenes from Childhood* Op. 15
Stravinsky *Petrushka* (ballet)
Tchaikowsky *The Nutcracker*

TRAINS
Honegger *Pacific 231*

Glen Miller *Chattanooga Choo-Choo*
Oscar Peterson *Night Train*
Johann Strauss *Train Polka*
Villa-Lobos *The Little Train of Carpira*

WATER
Bax *Tintagel*
Berlioz *Le Corsair* Overture Op. 21
Frank Bridge *The Sea* suite
Britten Sea Interludes from *Peter Grimes*
Britten *Four Sea Pictures* from *Peter Grimes*
Coates *By the Sleepy Lagoon* ("Desert Island Discs")
Debussy *L'Isle Joyeuse*
Debussy *La Mer*
Debussy *Petit Suite*
Debussy *Summer Night on the River*
Elgar *Sea Pictures* Op. 37
Ireland *Sea Idyll*
Mendelssohn *The Hebrides* overture
Mendelssohn *Calm Sea and Prosperous Voyage*
Respighi *The Fountains of Rome*
Smetana *Vltava*
Strauss *Blue Danube*
Vaughan Williams *Sea Symphony*
Walton *Portsmouth Point*

WEATHER
Beethoven *Symphony No. 6*
Borodin *In the Steppes of Central Asia*
Britten *Noyes Fludd*
Debussy *Children's Corner* suite
Mahler Slow Movement from *Symphony No. 9*
Meyerbeer *Les Patineurs* (ballet)
Strauss *Thunder and Lightning Polka*
Vaughan Williams *Sinfonia Antarctica*
Waldteufel *Skater's Waltz*

In addition to the music books already mentioned at the beginning of this chapter, the following publications have been found useful as a source for songs and supporting musical activity:

Music in action 3 Books William Bullman (Hart-Davis)
Children make music 3 books Dick Addison (Holmes McDougal)
Ears and Eyes Book I Jack Dobbs (O.U.P.)
Make music fun 4 books and teacher's book D. Maxwell-Timmins (Schofield & Sims)
Sounds and music Geoffrey Winters (Longman)

Note

When using recorded music for assemblies it is not sufficient just to play the music as the children file in and out of the assembly hall. This means that some children will only hear a few bars, since the last child in to the hall is usually the first out. One suggestion is, instead, to play an appropriate piece of music in the background, during creative writing lessons.